A TIBETAN MEDIC
TO HEALING ANXIETY, STF

MW00803782

HEALING ANXIETY

by

MARY FRIEDMAN RYAN, PHD

with

DR. (LADY) DADHON JAMLING
Personal Physician to
His Holiness the Dalai Lama

Born Perfect ink
ANCIENT WISDOM FOR MODERN TIMES
NORTHAMPTON, USA
WWW.BORNPERFECTINK.COM
WWW.HEALINGANXIETYBOOK.COM

Important: The information and techniques discussed in this book are based upon the personal and professional experiences and research of its author. The information contained in this book is not meant to be a substitute for medical care by a physician or other health care provider(s). Any diagnosis or medical care should be done under the guidance of a health care professional. The publisher does not promote the use of specific health care protocols but believes the information in this book should be made available to the general public. Neither the author nor the publisher assume any liability whatsoever for the use of the information contained in this book. The author and publisher strongly suggest consulting a professional health care provider about the appropriateness of any technique or procedure mentioned in this book.

TABLE OF CONTENTS

HOW TO USE THIS BOOK

TIBETAN BUDDHIST MEDICINE AND PSYCHIATRY EMPLOYS a holistic approach to healing stress and anxiety that combines herbal medicine, constitutional dietary advice, massage, moxibustion, healing exercises, and meditation. Tibetan doctors loosely define anxiety as *rLung* (pronounced loong), which means Wind. This book is a practical manual for healers and lay folk to learn and apply the gentle Tibetan medical treatments for healing *rLung*—soothing the mind, centering the body, and quieting the unleashed forces of Wind.

If you are suffering from anxiety, stress, or panic attacks, this book can launch you on your healing journey with very effective tools from Tibetan Medicine. After reading through these pages, you'll have a concrete understanding of *rLung* Imbalance, and you will be able to help yourself or your loved ones heal the symptoms of anxiety by utilizing this deep and wonderful ancient healing system. If you are a practitioner of Asian energy medicine, such as acupuncture and acupressure, this book will provide an understanding of how to heal or greatly improve your clients' *rLung* Imbalance based on what I learned from my years working with Dr. Dadhon Jamling and from my own Chinese Medicine practice.

Healing Anxiety is divided into two parts:

Part I is a discussion of the Tibetan medical way to bring calm and balance into your life. It provides case histories, a discussion of the theories and treatment strategies for *rLung* Imbalance, which causes anxiety, nervousness, and stress. This discussion is from my personal experience training in Dharamsala, India with several Tibetan doctors, lay healers, and the amazing Dr. Dadhon Jamling.

Part II is a reference section for how to identify and treat *rLung* Imbalance. Readers can refer to Part II while reading the first half of the book to get further details on treatments, such as meditations, massage techniques, dietary advice, etc. This section also includes a glossary of terms that you can reference. The Resources section contains references to get additional information about Tibetan Medicine supplies and Tibetan Medicine organizations.

On its own, no amount of technological development
can lead to lasting happiness.
What is almost always missing
is a corresponding inner development.

—His Holiness The Dalai Lama

FROM 1990 TO 1994, I LIVED AND WORKED IN the Himalayas in a tiny Tibetan clinic on the edge of a mountain. The town is called McLeod Ganj and is part of the larger community of Dharamsala, the seat of the Tibetan government in exile, where His Holiness the Dalai Lama lives. Dr. (Lady) Dadhon Jamling, a very well-known female Tibetan medical doctor educated at the highest level, was my research partner. We conducted research and saw over 45 patients per day. The clinic is a part of the Tibetan Medical and Astro. Institute, which has clinics serving Tibetan refugees all over India. I want to start you on your journey into understanding the Tibetan medical treatment of anxiety with a few case histories, where you can watch the treatments unfold. In this way, you will become familiar with this ancient and beautiful tradition. This section also introduces the theories behind Tibetan Medicine and treatment strategies for anxiety, nervousness, and stress. The last case history takes place in the United States, so you can see how we can bring these simple treatments to life in the West to solve one of the most commonly seen illnesses in most alternative medical practices . . .

PART I

STORIES OF HEALING

The mind affects the body,
and the body affects the mind.

—Dr. (Lady) Dadhon Jamling

ONE

STEWART'S ACUTE PANIC ATTACK

"This guy is really sick! I am way out of my league!" I think to myself as Dr. (Lady) Dadhon Jamling shoves an herbal pill into a bedraggled young man's mouth. He is stiff, flailing his arms a bit, and rocking back and forth, yet he somehow appears immobile at the same time. His groans are terrifying. He seems catatonic. I am guessing that he's around 24 years old and American. He strikes me as one of the many young, robust American men that come to Buddhist Dharamsala, the headquarters of the exiled Tibetan government in India, looking for answers to life through meditation, yoga, and extensive partying—an unhealthy combination, sometimes even lethal, for many young spiritual seekers.

Dr. Jamling picks up an incense stick she made earlier this week at her family's monastery. This incense is made from an ancient Tibetan medical formula that is the cornerstone of Tibetan medical treatments for anxiety and panic attacks, called *rLung*/Wind[1] disorder, believed to be a serious mental and physical imbalance in Tibetan Medicine. She lights the incense stick and waves it in front of the young man's nose. He groans again.

opposite:
The path to Dr. Jamling's clinic: my morning walk

3

"Put him on the table," she says strongly to me. "Mary! Put him on the table—do it!" But I freeze, unable to move, overwhelmed by the intensity of the scene unfolding before my eyes. She yells for more help, "Jamyang! Get over here!" Jamyang rushes in, looks at me serenely, and calmly smiles. He gently puts his hands underneath the American sitting stiffly on the bench between his two friends and a waiting Tibetan patient.

"Come on, Mary! You can do it!" Jamyang encourages. His voice jars me out of my dazed state, and I shove the terror of witnessing this extremely sick man into the denial corner of my mind. I start to move into action, and Jamyang and I get him onto the table.

A Young Oxford Student in Dharamsala

I am so new to this Tibetan clinic—a 25-year-old PhD student from Oxford studying medical anthropology and working full time in Dharamsala, India, researching Tibetan Medicine. I have been in Dharamsala for only one week on an internship of my own design—four days a week assisting in Dr. Jamling's clinic and one day a week working in the library at the Tibetan Medical and Astro. Institute. Although I attempted to study Tibetan before arriving, my language skills are limited to simple pleasantries and basic conversation.

Before the American's abrupt entrance into the clinic, Jamyang had just brought us tea. I remarked what a welcome break it was from the endless stream of sick patients, and Dr. Jamling said to me, smiling her wry smile, "You are young—why are you so tired?" It was only my third day in the clinic, and I had already seen over one hundred patients. I was so tired my body ached, and I needed more sleep. Mostly, I was energized and excited by what I was learning, but I was also in dire need of a nice hot "cuppa." I had wanted to give my mind a break from translating Tibetan constantly and perhaps relax and settle back into my own thoughts, preferably in my native language.

Our Humble Clinic

We were sitting at a table in Dr. Jamling's rickety, yellow wooden clinic that was perched precariously on the slope of the mountainside. To one side of the table stood a wall with one roughly hewn window, out of which we could see cows grazing below us. The view emphasized to me just how dangerously the clinic hung over the vast hillside.

Looking around the clinic, I realized there was not one wasted object in the space. Every piece of furniture was necessary, and many of the pieces, such as the old table where we wrote our notes, were handmade. There were two patient benches, the writing table, and an old rickety gurney with the wheels missing that I guessed to be a donation from a Western hospital from the 1940s. Also in the clinic was a beautiful Tibetan religious painting (called a *thangka*) of the blue Medicine Buddha presiding over our activity. In front of the *thangka* on a small table was some incense for morning offerings and Dr. Jamling's prayer beads. The clinic was an impeccably clean space thanks to Jamyang, the tall, willowy, and always smiling older Tibetan man, who happily kept us all stocked with tea and supplies as we worked.

Sitting and drinking my tea, I was wondering what was appropriate conversation at teatime with Dr. Jamling. I didn't have long to dwell on the problem, however, as Jamyang burst in.

Dr. Jamling's clinic in Dharamsala

The Impeccable Dr. (Lady) Dadhon Jamling

"Amchi-la! So very sorry! This one can't wait! They dragged him down the mountain; he cannot speak, and his mouth is frozen. His eyes are in a stiff stare. I think it might be *rLung*, *Amchi-la*, with all due respect." Jamyang says this all in Tibetan, and I can barely understand. I do know that "*Amchi-la*" refers to Dr. Jamling and is a respectful term for "doctor." I suddenly realize that I won't be drinking the rest of my lovely tea before me as I put my cup down and jump up to help.

Dr. (Lady) Dadhon Jamling

Dr. Jamling is young, perhaps 35 years old. She is a formally trained Tibetan medical doctor with a bright future ahead of her. (Several years later she becomes the first official female physician to the Dalai Llama and goes on to head the research department at the Tibetan Medical and Astro. Institute.) She is said to be one of the most beautiful women in town, full of grace, refinement, and knowledge. Her long hair is pinned up, and she wears the traditional Tibetan *chupa*, a long, wraparound dress with a V-neck. She is indeed a vision of beauty and movement.

This morning, like all other work days, Dr. Jamling left her four children with relatives at home, having fed them, having said her Medicine Buddha *puja* (ceremony) prayers, reconfirming her resolve to meet the challenges of medical practice all day long, with the compassion I know to be the signature of a Tibetan medical doctor. With her long dress scrunched up in one hand and her gray, sun-protecting parasol in the other, Dr. Jamling climbed the half mile up the dusty mountain path every morning to her clinic that seemed to hang over the cliff. She always arrived early with not a speck of dust on her, looking impeccable for work. I, in contrast, would arrive after the day had already begun in the clinic sweaty, dirty, and breathless from climbing up the steep mountain. I was in awe of Dr. Jamling's grace.

Panic Attack Treated the Tibetan Way

As she attends to the young man, Dr. Jamling remains her usual composed self.

"*She is so fearless!*" I think to myself as I watch her decidedly and calmly go about the task of reviving this horrifying stiff lump of a young man before us. His eyes are rigid and stare straight ahead. His mouth is open in a macabre, slanted O-shape. His arms are out in front of his body, and he is unable to lie down all the way. The only remote point of reference I have for this condition are my father's panic attacks, which I saw when I was a young child. But comparatively, this is much worse.

We sit the young man up on the gurney and instruct him to breathe in the smoke of the special stick of incense, but he remains unresponsive. His stiffness, his groans, and now his smell confirm my earlier thought: "*I am way out of my league!*" I am holding him with my arms on his back, and although I do somehow sense a small change in his breathing, the stiffness remains and he is unable to move. I can actually feel his terror, in a strange way. It's as if any movement at all would feel like death to him. Dr. Jamling talks as she moves around us. "This is an acute *rLung* problem," she says. I nod as I try to understand.

At this time, the only thing I know about *rLung* diseases is that they often have components of mental illness, tremors, paralysis, or severe anxiety and stiffness, as we are indeed seeing in this young man. The *rLung* (meaning life force) flows through channels, similar to *chi* (*qi*) flowing through the Chinese Medicine acupuncture meridians of the body. This is my first case of *rLung* disease, and things are happening very fast.

"Now swallow, boy. Come on, come on . . . swallow. Jamyang, let's get him some water . . . you will be all right, boy." Dr. Jamling is so soothing, she puts us all at ease. I feel somehow that I can trust her because she exudes this strong, all-knowing confidence.

Jamyang returns with the water, and we are able to guide a crushed herbal pill down the young man's throat. I find myself trying to be optimistic about the circumstances, talking to myself to stay hopeful: "*It's working its way down! Whatever was in that pill is now in his stomach.*"

However, his stiffness continues and time passes like molasses going uphill. We continue to hold the young man while Dr. Jamling begins to rhythmically chant a Medicine Buddha mantra.

Dr. Jamling catches my eye and says, "It's not working as fast as I had expected. We are going to give him herbs to strengthen the *rLung* medicine. We'll get him to breathe the herbs underneath a towel. It's more focused that way." Dr. Jamling turns, "Jamyang! Get the towel! Jamyang! Tell Dolma to get the herbs for *rLung*—the ones we burn—she knows—hurry Jamyang!"

But Jamyang is already out the door and no more than a minute passes before he and Dolma return together. Dolma works in the front of the small clinic as the herbal pharmacist. She is young, perhaps my age, and brings her baby boy Nyima to work daily. He plays happily in a cardboard box in the front of the clinic, where he is comforted by both employees and patients throughout the day.

Dolma in the apothecary

I watch as Dolma prepares the herbs in front of me, ties them quickly together with some twine, and places them in a bowl.

Suddenly, I realize that I may be of some small help after all. I say to the young man in English, "We're going to place this towel over your head so you can breathe in these herbs, okay? They will help you. Don't be frightened." I try to smile and nod to the young man.

Dr. Jamling quickly gets the towel situated over the young man, whose name we still do not know. She is humming pleasantly as she works. Lighting the herbs, she says something to herself in Tibetan that I cannot fully understand. It sounds to me like, "This had better work," and something else about the recipe from the *rGyud-bzhi* (pronounced gyu-shee), the main Tibetan medical text that is over a thousand years old. I later learn that she's saying a Tibetan Buddhist medicine prayer over the herbs before she uses them on her patient.

Dr. Jamling begins to appear mildly frustrated and exclaims, "What is going on?! Why isn't this working!" Thankfully, these words are barely out of her mouth when the young man begins to yawn.

"Yes! It's a yawn! The boy is yawning!"

"Keep breathing . . . That's it," Dr. Jamling encourages. "You are going to be fine . . . that's it . . . the *rLung* is going back to its proper places, boy. That's it, keep breathing, don't stop."

Calmness Returns

The young American relaxes more and starts to breathe heavily, then rhythmically, and we all sit in silence for some time. He stretches. Dr. Jamling takes the towel off his head, and he turns to look at me. His eyes have returned to the proper place in their sockets, and his identity emerges from within them. I have no idea how much time has passed. To me, it feels like an eternity of waiting and watching this surreal moment unfold before me. I feel just how American he is by his complete bewilderment of what has just happened. He twists around and stretches again, asking, "What happened to me?" Shuddering, he relaxes back into my arms, and I feel the weight of his supple body that now has some control over its movements. I initially feel anxious that he feels so comfortable with me holding him like this, since I have not yet settled into my professional role as a medical assistant.

He, on the other hand, doesn't seem bothered by my presence, so we just relax and smile together.

Dr. Jamling gently takes his wrist, feeling for his pulse. She asks, "What is your name?"

"Stew . . . Stewart . . . I . . . have never felt that way before," he stutters. "I couldn't get any words out, and my mind was racing. I felt completely trapped in my body . . . hysterical, frightened . . . like, I felt my body getting stiffer and stiffer . . . It was far out! My friends . . . where are they? I couldn't get any words out. Am I going to be okay?"

"You are okay. You're fine right now, but this is a very serious thing we need to watch," Dr. Jamling answers. She is referring to his *rLung* Imbalance, which according to Tibetan Medicine theory, can lead to full-blown psychosis in the most serious cases. "What have you been doing? This is something that can happen if your diet and your behavior are out of balance. Maybe you have been cold and a strong wind has been blowing on you. Also, I imagine you have been drinking a lot of alcohol and coffee. Maybe you have been meditating too much, or perhaps even thinking too much . . . "

Stewart blinks. "How did you know all that?" he replies. "It's true, all of it. We'd been partying for a few nights. A group of us were doing a meditation practice together, with breathing exercises to make the Kundalini rise."

"Aaaaah! That's it!" There is a glint of knowing in Dr. Jamling's eyes. "You know, this is very dangerous! If you awaken the *rLung* energy, it is like a wind. When you cannot control it, it can go into the wrong places in your body, into the wrong channels. This is something you shouldn't be doing, unless you have the proper conditions. Even well-trained monks can have this problem. The *rLung* can go into channels related to your consciousness, to your mind, and the flow of the *rLung* can get reversed. You see, the mind rides the *rLung*. It is like a horse. If the *rLung* goes out of control, so does your mind. In your case, there is other involvement as well, in the liver channel and the stomach. This is usually a combination of improper diet, improper sleep, living in a cold environment, and the breathing exercises that should only be practiced by monks, or at least with a teacher, and without any stimulants—like coffee, tea, and alcohol. You are lucky you came to me when you did."

Dr. Jamling is talking about *srog-rLung* (pronounced sok loong), a kind of acute anxiety that is both extremely serious and very frightening. In English we would call it, "life Wind" or "heart Wind." One of its symptoms is just what Stewart describes—a feeling of not being in one's own body, of not being oneself or feeling other than oneself, a severe feeling of detachment not only from others, but also from oneself. This type of *rLung* is brought on by over-doing certain behaviors over a period of time—behaviors like excessive worry, stress, over-work, sorrow, fear, anxiety, over thinking, and improper diet. If left untreated, the cycles of emotions become increasingly severe, going from sadness to elation and back again with increasing speed, until it turns into psychosis. There are certain pulse diagnoses and tongue diagnoses that can reveal the possible onset of *rLung* illness. One example is a huge, long crack down the center of the tongue, which, to my rookie amazement when I look, Stewart has.

Dr. Jamling takes her hand and puts it on his jaw, squeezing it. She turns his face, and looks into his eyes. She is carefully examining him, and he stares at her questioningly. I notice he is pleading with his eyes now, a new look of fear and understanding overtaking his countenance. He is grave. She sighs. She thinks for a moment, taps the table, and looks at him again with concern. She sighs again, takes a deep breath, and then exhales with what seems like some sort of resolve.

"Let's look at your back," she says, turning him around. I move off the table and also examine his back, wondering what she is doing, and what will be next. I look at Stewart, and realize he is probably thinking the same thing.

Moxibustion on Stewart's Back

In this clinic, time contracts and expands in strange ways: it feels as if ten minutes go by as Dr. Jamling stares at his back. *Amchi-la*, as I eventually learn to call her, always takes her time, carefully developing an elegant Tibetan medicinal treatment that combines diet, herbs, massage, acupuncture, and moxibustion.

Dr. Jamling's hand goes up to his neck and the other plods along his back, feeling various points along the spine with the first two fingers. She palpates four particular acupuncture points. The first is the cervical spine point at the nape of the neck called "point 1" in Tibetan Medicine. Then she moves further down, at the level of the fifth, sixth, and seventh thoracic vertebrae. Further still, her hand moves to the fourth lumbar vertebra. As she palpates these points, she asks, "Is this sensitive?. . . How about this one?" Stewart affirms that they are all sensitive. These points tend to be sensitive in *rLung* related illnesses, especially in the acute phase. Dr. Jamling takes a long, deep breath and pats his back. She turns him around and says, "Okay, these points are important for your treatment. I am going to give you some moxibustion, *Horgyi-metsa* (pronounced hor-gyay-met-za) as they say in Tibetan. I am going to burn a special herb, and then I am going to warm these points on your back. Please lie down."

Stewart nods, lies down on the gurney, and turns his face to me. Our eyes meet, and again I get the feeling that we are thinking the same thought: *What now?* However, there is such a sense of calm in the room that neither of us shows signs of nervousness. We do not smile but share an instant, supportive connection. We're both trying to hold it together during a tough time. Dr. Jamling interrupts our moment, "Mary! Run and get the *moxa* out of the cupboard in the next room." I jump, not used to being commanded in this direct way, but I quickly obey.

I reach the rickety glass doors of the cupboard and pull them open. Several brown paper bags with Tibetan writing on them are before me. The herb *moxa* is used for a healing technique called moxibustion. The herb is in the *Artemisia* genus, which is the same plant family as *Artemisia vulgaris* or mugwort. It's used in Asian medicine to warm the acupuncture points and channels that carry the *rLung* or *chi* (*qi*). I manage to read and comprehend the bags' labels. I come back with a wad of mugwort realizing the room is now completely filled with the smell of the *rLung* incense. It is steadily burning next to Stewart's head so that he can easily breathe it in. Through the breath, the herbal smoke stabilizes the *rLung* throughout the body's channels.

Stewart seems to be settling back into himself. Seeing the *rLung* go awry in this young man reinforces how powerful a force it truly is. I am beginning to understand how *rLung* disorders all have this quality of stress and tension, of jerkiness and intensity. Examples of *rLung* illnesses flow through my mind: anxiety, stress, Parkinson-like symptoms, Bell's Palsy-like deviations in the skin, and mental illnesses. Dr. Jamling's understanding of *rLung* amazes me.

Dr. Jamling rolls the tufts of mugwort and places them on top of square pieces of paper, which are folded into balls, then cut in half. She lights these moxa pieces and holds them directly on the acu-points for *rLung* Imbalance. The smell reminds me of an odd mix of autumn leaves and black tar. Dr. Jamling quickly pulls the burned *moxa* off the point just before the fire nears the skin. When she performs this process, known as moxibustion, she sometimes uses needles with balls of mugwort stuck on the ends. However, this time she chooses the rolled-paper method and slowly moves from one acu-point to the next. As he is receiving moxibustion, Stewart talks with us. "I still feel really strange. My eyesight is weird, and I feel like I am a little outside of myself, like I am trying to feel something, but it's not... it's not... registering..." Dr. Jamling listens and nods.

Amchi-la is so very soothing with him. All of her movements, all of her words are well thought out, kind, and evoke great equanimity. She tells Stewart, "The *rLung* carries your Mind and your emotions, too. You must give it time. Do not worry. I think we can help you. You just must give it some time and be gentle on yourself. I am going to write you a prescription for herbal pills . . . You may get up now."

Stewart rises and turns. "Will . . . will this happen again?" He asks warily, appearing deeply frightened, as if he is afraid of the answer.

She answers quickly, "It depends . . . it could. I do not know. You have to be very careful with your diet. No pork. No cold drinks. No coffee. No alcohol. I also don't want you meditating or trying to control your breath. Try to keep your thoughts very simple, free of worry. Do things you enjoy and remain thinking about the present moment. The past and the future can cause you great anxiety. Right now is a time just to take care, to relax yourself . . . "

Stewart interrupts, "How come this didn't happen to my friends?"

"You have the typical bodily constitution for *rLung* problems. You are not so tall, and you are dark and wiry. This can mean you are more susceptible. People who have the *rLung* constitution are very intelligent. They have very fast minds and are quick to anger. That's the general idea, you know . . . maybe your friends are fat! Ha-ha! Or maybe they eat different foods. Your mind works very fast—I can feel its speed in your pulse. You need a calm environment, not so much meditating. Your mind is going too fast to be off breathing, meditating, and exciting your *rLung*."

"Am . . . I crazy? I felt like I was going crazy..." Stewart looks down, barely able to get the words out.

"No . . . even highly-educated monks get this problem. We Tibetans don't think like that so much. We focus more on relaxing and not exciting the *rLung*. Don't worry too much about it or be so hard on yourself." Dr. Jamling touches his arm and smiles. "These herbal pills will settle the *rLung* into its proper places. I need you to see me every few days or so . . . and I will give you this incense. Every morning and evening at the time of *rLung*, you should breathe it in. It will calm your mind and body."

"How much will that cost? I barely have any money," he quietly says.

"You pay what you can. At least, I hope you can afford the herbal pills. They will cost you about... (she pauses)... three dollars." Dr. Jamling says this with a wide smile. She later tells me that she loves saying this to the foreigners, who are used to paying unearthly medical bills in Western hospitals.

For the first time Stewart smiles, too. "I think I can handle that."

Teatime Again

A sense of calm envelops the clinic once again. Stewart swings his legs off the table, leans to get up and says, "I can't thank you enough…" Dr. Jamling now looks up at Stewart for the first time—he is stretched to his full height and is taller than she. She bows ever so slightly and smiles. They share a nice moment of silence together. I quietly watch and listen from a distance, a technique I find to be quite useful in this clinical setting, where so many come to unload their life's burdens on her.

As Stewart thanks her, we hear giggling and look behind us. Two Tibetan children are being pulled back by an elderly woman standing in the doorway. There's never a lot of time for privacy here, but there is always a sense of respect. A young woman, perhaps 20, pushes through and says, "Stew—are you okay?" She has long, blonde dreadlocks, cannot weigh much more than 100 pounds, and wears a long, shaggy torn dress. They embrace, and she guides Stewart toward the door.

Stewart turns back and says again, "I can't thank you enough, Doctor." Dr. Jamling and I can see a pure intelligence in his eyes now, and his wits are acute. He looks contained. We confirm this to one another when we discuss his case later that day.

Dr. Jamling waves her hand in response, saying, "Just make sure I see you in a few days—and no pork! No coffee! No alcohol!"

When they are gone, *Amchi-la* frets silently to herself, only noticeable to me by her furrowed brow. She furtively rubs her prayer beads in her hand, seemingly giving over her worries to the Medicine Buddha who presides over us and all Tibetan medical clinics. She sighs and collects herself for the next wave of patients. She calls Jamyang for new, hot tea, and flashes me her wide smile.

Health and happiness are the rights of every individual.
That is why it is important to encourage the promotion
of different healing systems, such as the Tibetan,
that are traditional and ancient. Their importance
in contributing substantially towards medical sciences,
particularly in the field of psychosomatic medicine,
and non-infectious diseases, should not be ignored.

—His Holiness the Dalai Lama

TWO

BEHIND THE ANCIENT CURTAIN:
MY OWN JOURNEY WITH ANXIETY

After the American Stewart left Dr. Jamling's clinic, I had many unanswered questions:

What was in the herbal pill that Dr. Jamling gave him?

How can burning an herb on one's back calm the mind?

How does inhaling incense affect the mind?

And whoever thought pork could affect one's emotions?

The answers to these questions and more lie in an ancient medical tradition that began centuries ago in one of the most mysterious places on earth—Tibet.

My Awakening

I first encountered Tibetan Medicine when I was in graduate school on track to become a Western medical doctor. I was working in a nursing home as a nurse's aide. One day, Dr. Yeshe Dhonden, a Tibetan medical doctor, visited our facility just outside of Oxford, England.

Someone on the staff told us that Dr. Dhonden could diagnose patients' illnesses just by looking at their urine bags, reading their pulses at the wrist, and looking at the patients' tongues. I chuckled

opposite: The townsfolk lining the street, welcoming His Holiness the Dalai Lama back from abroad.

17

when I heard this. I was a very skeptical pre-med student working on a master's degree in human biology. However, I decided this notion was very entertaining indeed, so I followed the Tibetan doctor around as he walked from bed to bed. To my utter shock and disbelief, and with no previous knowledge of any of the patients, he diagnosed them correctly—12 out of 12 patients—he nailed every single patient!

I decided right then and there that I needed to know more about this ancient "Tibetan Medicine." I was instantly fascinated with its subtlety and preciseness. There was clearly not one healing system in the world, but lots of very different healing systems. This little event, on this very ordinary day, radically changed the direction of my studies and eventually the course of my life's work. Dr. Dhonden practices Tibetan Medicine in Dharamsala, India and is the author of *Health Through Balance: An Introduction to Tibetan Medicine* and *Healing from the Source: The Science and Lore of Tibetan Medicine*. Thank you, Dr. Dhonden, for that amazing day in Oxford.

After receiving my master's in human biology, I switched to the field of biological and medical anthropology, hoping to eventually understand Tibetan Medicine from a scientific viewpoint. As a PhD candidate at Oxford University, I decided to embark on what I thought was going to be a short stint of fieldwork in Dharamsala. As a medical anthropologist, I intended to use the biomedical measurement tools to gauge the efficacy of the Tibetan treatment of hepatitis. I spent a total of nine weeks in Dharamsala, working beside two Tibetan medical doctors and observing the treatment of patients with acute hepatitis. Back then, it was commonly known in India that Tibetan Medicine could "cure" acute hepatitis quite easily, and thus limit the debilitating recovery of the disease that is treated with just aspirin and bedrest in Western hospitals. I was intrigued to say the least.

Despite my best efforts and intentions, my efficacy study fell apart. The first hard challenge I faced was that the Tibetan patients refused to let me draw their blood, thus limiting my measurement tools significantly. Secondly, many of the subjects just dropped out of the study entirely. It is hard to measure a study of patients if you do not have any patients to measure! It was a minor disaster, but I learned from the experience and moved on.

Subsequently, I researched the efficacy of Tibetan medical treatments for arthritis, developing new protocols for rigorously measuring a non-Western medical system's healing modalities. Nine weeks in Northern India turned into six four-month visits, spending every summer I could running small scientific studies, shadowing Tibetan doctors, and writing up research and efficacy notes, totaling hundreds and hundreds of pages. During these years, Dr. Jamling and I developed three main studies: one on over 1600 clinical case histories, giving an overview of what Tibetan Medicine can treat; one on Tibetan treatments for arthritis; and a post-doctoral study of PTSD among Tibetan refugees and how Tibetan Medicine helped them.

Sleepless in Dharamsala

Tibetan Medicine's power to heal anxiety hit home personally when I was confronted with my own health crisis. I, too, suffered from anxiety during my fieldwork days in Dharamsala. I was putting in long 12-hour work days, not eating properly, nor drinking enough fluids. One night, I lay in bed, restless, anxious, and unable to sleep. I tossed and turned and drifted in and out of nightmares, fearful that I was incapable of finishing my PhD research with Dr. Jamling. Many a night ensued with the same fears and sleeplessness. I would be fine in the day when I was working, then night after night I would be haunted by my restless, anxious demons: thoughts of failure terrorizing me until the next morning. I tried to rationalize with myself that it was because I was somewhat isolated, living alone in a foreign country. I felt anxious and overwhelmed at times, but no amount of overwork could persuade me that I deserved a day off. That I could even take a day off was not an option.

As my symptoms grew worse, I sometimes found it difficult to concentrate, which I feared would start to affect my fieldwork. I was fiercely overworked: tired, jagged, not always making sense to myself. I often couldn't see the forest for the trees—I lacked a kind of serenity that allowed me to sit back and make good research decisions. I was constantly over-thinking everything and second-guessing myself. I had heart palpitations and fear with no name. As dusk fell, I started to dread the looming night ahead. These symptoms increased exponentially until finally, they led me to seek out help from a Tibetan doctor. I didn't want to jeopardize my professional relationship with Dr. Jamling, so I sought help from another Tibetan doctor at first.

Although Stewart and I had what seemed to be very different symptoms, they were of the same origin—just juxtaposed along a different spectrum: we both had *rLung* Imbalance, but mine was a much milder case, while his was a very serious full-blown panic attack that looked almost catatonic. The doctor prescribed Dr. Jamling's special incense and an herbal remedy called Eaglewood 35 pills.[1] He gave me a strict diet of no spicy food, no cold food, no cold drinks, and, much to my dismay, no coffee. He also recommended that I do meditation exercises, which were available for free in the Tibetan Library every morning. This course of action gave me the strength to change the bad habits I had developed from overworking and ignoring my body's need for a healthier lifestyle.

After my appointment with the Tibetan doctor, I curtailed my intake of coffee, followed his advice, and embarked on a meditation course for "inner development." This Tibetan approach to anxiety really taught me how to manage the telltale signs of *rLung* Imbalance: anxiety, stress, fatigue, and insomnia. To this day when the *rLung* occasionally flares-up, I have learned how to deal with it by curtailing my caffeine intake, training my mind to remain in the present moment, using food to balance the three humors, and occasionally adding incense and massage into the mix. Thanks to Tibetan Medicine, I have never again experienced that overwhelming anxiety since those nights in Dharamsala.

Harnessing the Wind

The Tibetan doctor recognized my symptoms as the classic symptoms of *rLung* Imbalance. The Tibetan word *rLung* means "Wind" or "movement" and is one of three main energetic forces that constitute the basis of Tibetan medical physiology. These three forces (called "humors") are: *rLung* (Wind), *Tipa* (Bile), and *Bad-Gan* (Phlegm). The properties of *rLung* are similar to the properties of the wind: it is invisible, yet one can feel its movement throughout the body. As suggested by the term "movement," *rLung* is responsible for the coursing of blood, other fluids, and nutrients throughout the body. The *rLung* is free to move through the channels flowing throughout the body and is similar to the concept of *chi* in Chinese Medicine, which also involves a system of acupuncture channels through which a subtle, vital force flows.

The *rLung* energy is like the wind blowing through the trees—you cannot see it, but you can observe its subtle effects.

Dr. Jamling explains the nature of *rLung* as follows:

> In explaining *rLung* and the mind's relationship to it, one can think of our mind as riding a horse, and *rLung* is the horse. It is a very subtle relationship illustrated in this traditional Buddhist story: A man is riding a horse that is galloping very quickly around, going hither and thither. Another man, standing not too far away from him, yells, "Where are you going?" The man on the horse yells back, "I don't know! Ask the horse!" The moral of the story is that we shouldn't be asking ourselves how the horse is doing, but rather, we should be in control of the horse. So our mind rides a horse called *rLung*. If we do not control the *rLung* and it runs into the improper channels or places it shouldn't go, it can wreak havoc on both our mind and body. It is all about respect and control.

Tibetan doctors understand the subtle forces of nature and how they affect the brain, thought processes, breathing, and the biological processes of the body. An imbalance of *rLung* can underlie many diseases, and understanding and respecting the nature of *rLung* is a vital part of being a good Tibetan medical doctor.

Ancient Tibetan scriptures detailing the manifestation of *rLung* disease led to the chapter on *rLung* disease contained in the sacred *rGyud-bzhi* (pronounced gyu-shi), the main Tibetan medical text that is still in use today. This *rGyud-bzhi* chapter is taught in Tibetan medical schools today and provides the foundational understanding for the treatment of *rLung* disease.

The *rLung* Imbalance symptoms are many: anxiety, restless sleep, paranoia, an inability to concentrate, emotional instability, unmotivated irritability, pain in the neck, moving pain throughout the body,

Symptoms of *rLung* Imbalance

According to Dr. Jamling, when *rLung* is disturbed in a person, any of the following symptoms can occur:

- Difficulty concentrating, talking a lot, laughing and crying for no reason, mental instability, loss of self control
- Cannot sleep deeply, insomnia
- Anxiety, sighing, dizziness, buzzing or muffled sounds in the ears, or tinnitus (ringing in the ears)
- Continuous yawning, trembling, or unmotivated irritability
- Legs and feet feel very heavy and painful as if the bones are fractured; swelling or numbness in lower body
- Contracted limbs (extremities and limbs start to curl up and into the body), rigid and stiff limbs, or the wish to stretch the limbs
- The skin pulled taught over the surface of the body (like Rheumatoid Arthritis), sensations as if one's limbs were tightly bandaged
- Shifting pain all over the body that comes and goes in different places without any apparent physical cause, sharp pains during movement
- Lack of any movement, catatonic, staring at nothing, weak, losing memory, can occur after a shocking incident
- Cold shivering or formation of goosebumps
- Painful sensations produced by the clothes touching one's body hair or a painful sensation as if the skin was separated from the flesh
- A painful sensation in the eyes as if they were about to exit from their sockets
- Cough caused by a sensation of an obstruction in the throat
- Swelling that is not pitted (when you press into it, it bounces right back), much hunger, stress, and tension
- Abdominal distention and intestinal rumblings
- Reddish, dry, and/or rough tongue or an astringent taste in the mouth

or even tremors. Overall, one feels anxious and emotionally imbalanced with some bodily pain and other inexplicable symptoms. When suffering from a *rLung* Imbalance, anxiety and stress are the most common symptoms. A long term, serious *rLung* Imbalance can result in symptoms similar to those seen in Western psychosis. In the case of extreme anxiety, the movement of *rLung* speeds up, increasing to the point of spilling beyond the channels in which it usually travels, thereby creating chaos throughout the body/mind.

What happens when *rLung* runs rampant in a person? The mind becomes untethered, and the person experiences a general feeling of anxiety and restlessness. Sleep is disturbed, small details are irritating, and daily life tasks seem monumental. If *rLung* is out of balance, the state of a person's mental health is, too. The *rLung* energy is the force in the body that carries our thoughts and our consciousness. It is only when *rLung* goes into the wrong places that it can wreak havoc on our system, thus also affecting the mind. There can also be a lack of *rLung*, which is very rare. An imbalance of *rLung* usually involves an excess of *rLung* and more than one organ system.

The Path to Follow: Healing *rLung* Imbalance and Anxiety

Contained in the ancient Tibetan medical teachings are road maps to a calmer mind and body dynamic. Tibetan doctors give exercises to equalize the flow of *rLung* in the subtle channels in the body, all originating from Buddhist scriptures on the stabilization of the mind. Depending on the problem, they also give simple prescriptions: herbal pills, diet, and aromatherapy using the special *rLung* incense—bringing the body back to equilibrium, and thus calming the mind.

In Tibetan Medicine, treatment is multidimensional in nature. It can involve any combination of some or all of the following healing modalities:

Acupressure and Massage—Using massage with oils and pressure on corresponding *rLung* points in the Tibetan channel system. *See Chapter 10 for more information about Tibetan massage.*

Dietary Advice—Correcting dietary indiscretions and utilizing

Causes of *rLung* Imbalance

"These symptoms are usually most aggravated in the evening and around dawn," explains Dr. Jamling. She further describes the causes of *rLung* Imbalance in general. "If one is suffering from *rLung*, the causes can be many," she explains. The following are the main issues that Dr. Jamling says cause the *rLung* to get disturbed or agitated:

- Overworking, especially on an empty stomach
- A diet consisting of large quantities of foods that are not nutritious (e.g. junk food, fast food, and highly processed foods)
- A diet based on foods that have a bitter taste, such as coffee or black tea (green and white tea do not aggravate *rLung* symptoms)
- An excess of food with a light and rough quality, such as sugar or rice
- A diet of fried foods
- Drinking cold water in excess (iced drinks)
- Excessive sexual intercourse, which incites the *rLung* because it is housed in the area around the perineum
- Not sleeping well, which affects the movement of *rLung* through the channels of the body
- Some sicknesses, which can affect the *rLung* so that it becomes a chronic disease, such as hemorrhage due to bleeding, strong diarrhea, and vomiting
- Immense grief, for example, crying to the point of exhaustion
- Sorrow connected to emotional situations and experiencing shock
- Great mental activity, for example, an excessive exertion in study or in business

food as a form of medicine. *See Chapter 9 for a discussion of different dietary approaches to healing rLung Imbalance.*

Meditation–Tibetan medical texts also recommend meditation, as well as breathing and yoga exercises to help calm the mind. *For more information about meditations for healing rLung Imbalance, see Chapter 8.*

Aromatherapy–Dr. Jamling prescribes her handmade *rLung* incense that pacifies *rLung* and soothes the mind. One must simply breathe in the incense, allowing the smoke of the herbs to enter the channels through the lung membranes. *For more information about this incense, please see the Resources.*

Lifestyle Advice–Tibetan Medicine also prescribes various changes in lifestyle, suggesting healing exercises for the body, changing habits that might be harmful, or changing routines. Tibetan doctors strive to help patients understand *rLung* when it arises, and how to recognize it so that they can identify for themselves when they need to make lifestyle changes. It's also important that clients develop an understanding of their own constitution, eating a proper diet, adding meditation and exercises to their routines as a way of life. *See Chapter 11 for more information about Tibetan healing exercises.*

Moxibustion–Although acupuncture is rarely used in Tibetan Medicine, treatment with moxibustion is common for *rLung* Imbalance. To receive this treatment, see a Tibetan Medicine practitioner. *For more information about moxibustion, see Chapter 12.*

Herbal Medicine–A Tibetan Medicine doctor can also prescribe herbal pills, mainly the Tibetan herbal pill named Eaglewood 35, which has over 35 ingredients. *See Resources for more information about this pill and its herbal ingredients.*

Tibetan Medicine Comes West

The ancient Buddhist scriptures explain ways of controlling the breath and thus controlling the mind, as the two are inextricably linked. Through proper breathing and meditation instruction, one's mind can become calm and serene. The mind rides the *rLung*. If you use your mind to harness the *rLung*, then the *rLung* is kept under control and can't wreak havoc on your various organ systems. Through breath work and meditation, the *rLung* is settled into its proper channels, and you feel relaxed.

Tibetan doctors and monks have also discovered how the *rLung*, or vital force, can go awry through the misuse of meditation techniques and deleterious breath work. Since the mind is so inextricably linked to the breath, Dr. Jamling sees a number of Westerners who through forced "chakra" breathing exercises can end up with severe mental illness. This is because the forced breath work causes the *rLung* energy to go into the wrong channels, or even reverses the direction of the flow of energy, resulting in madness in the mind and chaos in the body. Dr. Jamling explains:

Westerners tend to lean towards an "easy" road to enlightenment. They attend a workshop or retreat whereby they can open their higher energy centers, or chakras, through specific breath work. This is a very esoteric, secret teaching meant for monks on the highest level of Buddhist awakening practice . . .

The problem is that if you open the chakra too early, when your mind still contains residues of negativity and

You cannot cheat the rLung. This causes serious mental illness.

you haven't worked through your karma, your discipline, and purity of the mind . . . if you haven't done this work, and you open your centers, then you open up too early to a world where all your subconscious negative thoughts and fears are let loose on your whole physiological system. You cannot cheat the *rLung*. This causes mental illness, and is very serious . . . Fortunately, we are able to help such patients.

Tibetan medical doctors strongly urge Westerners to avoid such intense workshops or retreats. They also encourage people who have done extensive and potentially damaging breath work to consult their practitioner as soon as possible as they are often able to settle the *rLung* energy back into the proper channels, and equilibrium of the mind can once again be achieved.

Tibetan Medicine Illuminated

In 1998, His Holiness the Dalai Lama attended The First International Congress on Tibetan Medicine held in Washington, DC. Addressing the conference, he said:

I am very grateful to see this dialogue develop between Tibetan and Western medical doctors . . . I would just like to correct the title of this conference. The first international congress on Tibetan Medicine was held in the 7th century.

Tibetan Medicine has one of the oldest written research traditions in the world. His Holiness the Dalai Lama was referring to the irony of a young and newly founded country, the United States of America, thinking it is leading the cutting edge of research into medicine, when, in fact, Tibetan Medicine is much, much older than any modern biomedicine. Written clinical case histories, research, and herbal formulas can be traced back to the 7th century and even earlier. Tibetan medical doctors still use the wisdom of their famous doctors from hundreds of years ago and still refer back to the written advice in ancient manuscripts to aid in the treatment of difficult cases seen in the modern world today.

Tibetan Medicine is a widespread medical system known for having doctors that treat patients all over Asia, including Tibet, China, Mongolia, Nepal, Sikkim, Bhutan, Ladakh, Northern India, East Turkestan, and other parts of Central Asia and Russia. Historically, a Tibetan medical doctor undertook six to seven years of full-time training. Tibetan doctors train in Buddhist religious doctrines related to the nature of the mind and psychology. Similar to other Asian medical systems, they also train to diagnose illness through taking pulses at the radial artery on each wrist.

Examinations of the color, coating, shape, and marks on the tongue are also studied. However, unlike other Asian medical systems, Tibetan doctors also examine the color and quality of the patient's urine. They believe much can be learned from such examinations.

Tibetan medical practices are indeed slowly influencing Western culture with large centers in the Netherlands, Switzerland, and France, as well as a medical college in the United States. Research on the efficacy of Tibetan Medicine is currently being undertaken in universities worldwide, and the conversation between Eastern and Western trained doctors is well underway. The Dalai Lama promotes Tibetan medicine's extensive knowledge of pyschosomatic medicine and collaborates with researchers at Harvard University and elsewhere to spread and further the importance of Tibetan Medicine for

today's illnesses. Aspects of Tibetan Buddhist medicine have seen some successes in the West. For example, the meditation exercises used for stress are being adapted to Western culture by being boiled down to simple, non-sectarian methods called Mindfulness Based Stress Reduction or MBSR. Several biomedical studies have shown that MBSR is statistically and significantly effective in reducing depression, chronic pain, anxiety, and mental stress. *See Resources for more information about MBSR.*

How Nine Weeks Becomes Six Years

Nine weeks in Dharamsala soon became six years of spending as much time there as grants and service projects would allow me. I finished my PhD at Oxford and continued my studies with a post-doctoral research project. During that time in Dharamsala, there was a huge influx of Tibetan refugees arriving from Tibet with acute Post Traumatic Stress Disorder (PTSD). This was casued by the trauma and violence they had undergone and the difficulties of the months-long trek across the mountains from Tibet to India.

The World Health Organization was conducting a study in Dharamsala on PTSD at the time. Psychiatrists from the West trained in biomedicine were being flown in to treat Tibetan refugees suffering from symptoms of PTSD. They wanted to train Tibetan medical doctors to recognize the symptoms of PTSD and then refer Tibetan patients to Western doctors who could prescribe free pharmaceuticals. It seemed short sighted to me that the Western doctors were trying to treat the Tibetans for PTSD. Their project seemingly overlooked the already well-established Tibetan Medical procedures for handling acute anxiety and PTSD symptoms—or *rLung* Imbalance. I was shocked at how little respect was given to local Tibetan medical culture. Tibetan Medicine wasn't even factored into the implementation of the World Health Organization guidelines for treating PTSD in Dharamsala. In my training as a medical anthropologist, this was a clear example of a foreign power coming in and not respecting a local indigenous medical system. I decided to apply for grant money from various aid organizations to study and document Tibetan medical treatments for PTSD, anxiety, and stress, from the Tibetan point of view.

Could we show the benefits of Tibetan Medicine from a scientific viewpoint for the benefit of Tibetans as well as the World Health Organization? I felt compelled to do this study to advocate on behalf of the Tibetan medical doctors, who ironically were genuinely excited about the Western medical techniques for treating PTSD and wanted to cooperate with Western doctors. Unfortunately, the Western doctors weren't curious at all about the Tibetan medical techniques. It was clearly not an equal exchange of opinions.

Supported by the Danish aid organization, Danida, the Carlsberg Foundation, and the World Health Organization, this small postdoc study allowed me to concentrate more specifically on *rLung* and mental health in Tibetan Medicine. Together, Dr. Jamling and I documented the case histories of over 40 patients suffering from *rLung*

Imbalance and followed their treatment over a period of eight weeks. We agreed that if we could document the efficacy of Tibetan medical treatments for *rLung* Imbalance, perhaps we could gain funding to support other Tibetan clinics that were greatly overburdened with the newly arriving Tibetan refugees. We also hoped to establish Tibetan Medicine as a legitimate medical system in the eyes of Western medicine, with effective remedies for mental illness—including symptoms similar to PTSD—for treatment of their own patients.

Our results were hopeful, showing that Tibetan Medicine was, indeed, helpful for these 40 patients. We documented that most of the patients were brought back to stable mental health from alarming levels of anxiety (*rLung*) with the use of simple, inexpensive behaviors: acupressure, moxibustion, diet, and herbal remedies. We knew that our work could be used to help future patients suffering from *rLung*-related symptoms and believed that more in-depth, case-controlled research with larger sample sizes was warranted to show the scientific community that Tibetan *rLung* treatments were beneficial for PTSD. I am happy to say that our small study did, indeed, lead to further research and support for Tibetan medical doctors in the eyes of the world.

This kind of research isn't just important for the acceptance of Tibetan Medicine from Western doctors. It is vital for helping Westerners heal from acute anxiety disorders. When Dr. Jamling visited me a few years ago in the United States, she remarked, "Wow—there is so much *rLung* in your culture!" And we laughed together because she was so right. There is so much *rLung* Imbalance in our culture. And no cure. Tibetan Medicine has the cure.

I fondly remember the early days spent steeped for hours in the tiny Tibetan medical clinic perched high on a cliff, observing what I came to realize were perhaps the best doctors—East or West—I had ever witnessed. It confirmed for me the need to further my research on Tibetan Medicine, and so I continue to ever expand my knowledge today.

Dr. Jamling Today

Dr. Dadhon Jamling visited us in the United States in 2007. At that time, Dr. Jamling was the head of research at the Tibetan Medical and Astro. Institute (*Men-Tsee-Khang*) in Dharamsala, India. Our research together helped launch a new generation of papers, presentations, and the cross-fertilization of Western and Tibetan medical approaches to disease across many disciplines, establishing the Tibetan Medical and Astro. Institute (TMAI) as a legitimate medical research facility. The TMAI now has its own journal, with publications of peer-reviewed, case-controlled trials of very effective Tibetan medical treatments. Dr. Jamling pursued both research and clinical practice for over ten years. Then, she was chosen to become the first woman to be a Personal Physician to His Holiness, the Dalai Lama. Dr. Jamling has retired from working at the TMAI, but still works for His Holiness, part time.

One can think of our mind as riding a horse,
and *rLung* is the horse.

— *Dr. (Lady) Dadhon Jamling*

THREE

HEALING LOBSANG'S PTSD

When Tashi Delek Lobsang, a thirty-one-year-old monk, came to the clinic during our *rLung* study, I recognized him immediately. He was the warmly-smiling man I passed daily in the narrow, muddy streets of Dharamsala.

He always remembers everyone's name and greets them as they pass by. He is tall, angular in build, and strong. He is fit, and his body shows the health and vigor of a monk who wakes up early. His days are filled with the simple, physical labors of maintaining a fully-operational monastery. He is generous, very reliable, and a true scholar of Tibetan Buddhism. Many people respect him for his impressive debating skills.

Lobsang tells us that he cannot fall asleep easily and startles awake often during the night. He has ominous feelings of dread and fear, especially around dawn and dusk, which is the circadian rythm of *rLung*. He says he feels anxious when embarking upon simple tasks. These tasks could include meeting a new person, buying food at the market, or even tutoring his students at the monastery.

opposite: Tibetan *puja* ceremony at His Holiness the Dalai Lama's monastery called Namgyal in Dharamsala

Transitions are difficult for him: starting a conversation, walking into a room, going into the sleep world, etc. This is typical of *rLung* Imbalance. The anxiety makes transitions difficult. His anxiety mani-

This is typical of rLung Imbalance. The anxiety makes transitions difficult.

fests with severe heart palpitations, breathlessness, and thoughts of bad things happening that he knows to be unrealistic or untrue. He cannot control his thoughts at these acute times, in spite of his intense meditation training, and this frustrates him even more. He talks to us about his feelings of dread for the future, and although he knows they have no ground, they possess him, and limit his lifestyle as a monk. He doesn't know what to do.

We cannot fully understand Lobsang's case without also knowing his history. Upon interviewing him, we learn that he escaped Chinese-occupied Tibet one year prior and made the grueling months-long journey to Dharamsala. He walked almost the entire way, which would be almost 1000 miles. Lobsang tells us of his journey:

> I was with three other people, and we had very little money. We slept, hidden, during the day, and traversed hilly dangerous territory at night, constantly worried about being caught . . . I worried so much about my friends and that if we were caught that we would get the other people who helped us on the way in trouble, too . . . At the border we all separated. It was the safest way. But then we were unable to find one of our friends again, and we have not heard from him since . . .

When Lobsang arrived in Dharamsala, he was welcomed into one of the local monasteries with a letter from a previous teacher that he had carried with him. While this was comforting, he still struggled to re-establish himself in a new city, as a refugee monk. Lobsang had to work very hard to prove himself and to keep up with his studies. He also had to learn English, do many new chores unfamiliar to him, and overcome the great loneliness that he felt. Lobsang succeeded, yet it seemed to take a great toll on his health. Constant overwork, worry, and denying himself simple pleasures for months on end ultimately led to the worsening of his symptoms.

Lobsang's Symptoms

Lobsang's physical symptoms are common for *rLung* Imbalance. He complains of physical pain traveling throughout his body, like small lightning shocks with an odd sensation of numbness in his skin. When he awakens during the night from pain, he is unable to go back to sleep. He also tells us of severe constriction at the nape of his neck and a feeling of fullness in his chest, as though he cannot breathe. It helps him to take in large gulps of air, and to arch his back, stretch, and release the feeling of tightness around his chest. When he experiences the heart palpitations, the constriction in his voice and in his chest, as well as the pain in his neck, all intensify. Sometimes the worsening mental anxiety and the painful bodily sensations hurl him into a full-blown panic attack. The "time" when *rLung* symptoms are usually at their worst is at dawn and dusk, when Lobsang feels the most anxiety. He also complains of epigastric pain, gurgling in his stomach, and acid indigestion. This happens when he forgets to eat.

EXAMINING LOBSANG MORE CLOSELY

During his evaluation by Dr. Jamling, I watch as she takes his pulse on his wrist and confirms that it is "empty," which means it disappears with pressure. She explains that an empty pulse feels like a small bubble floating on the water.

She points out that his tongue is reddish pink and peeled, with no coating on it. There is very little to almost no moisture on his tongue. His urine reveals *rLung* issues as well; it is clear, watery, and tinged with a bit of a blue. His skin and hair are rough to the touch, dry, brittle, and in desperate need of some moisturizer. In Tibetan Medicine, the lungs and the skin are believed to be one single organ that suffers when there is a lack of proper circulation of *rLung* in the chest. When *rLung* is out of balance, it can cause dryness in the body.

Dr. Jamling announces her diagnosis of *rLung* disturbance. She says the *rLung* is like the wind and can get stirred up. Lobsang's *rLung* has moved out of its resting places, first invading the stomach channels and now working its way up and affecting the area around the heart. Lobsang confirms her diagnosis, saying that at first, it was mainly stomach problems that debilitated him, along with the obsessive worrying over small details that seemed to increase over time, making transitions difficult and filling him with fear and dread.

In order to treat Lobsang's *rLung* Imbalance, Dr. Jamling explains to me that we must pacify *rLung* by focusing on the areas in which it has invaded: the stomach and the heart. Interestingly enough, Dr. Jamling does not prescribe the usual *rLung* herbal pill medication. She believes that we can heal Lobsang just through the use of food, moxibustion, massage, and some practical advice. His strong demeanor, straightforward honesty, and the strength in his eyes and voice say to Dr. Jamling that this is a patient whom the *rLung* has not "completely possessed."

Lobsang's "Prescription"

Here is the complete "prescription" for treating Lobsang with explanations where needed:

Dr. Jamling recommends that Lobsang eat nutritious foods such as meat, especially beef and lamb. Fish is also particularly good because of its oils (the oils will help Lobsang's dryness because they moisturize the interior of the body), and it can be fried. She also recommends Lobsang drink nettle tea along with eating some nettles cooked lightly in pepper, which anchors the *rLung* and helps settle the energy into its resting places.[1] Rice, first cooked and then fried in butter, is also a staple food to pacify *rLung*; other ingredients can be added to it, such as garlic, onion, and ginger, all of which pacify *rLung*. Lobsang's case involves the heart channels, so Dr. Jamling emphasizes the use of angelica root in stews, salads, and rice. Sunflower seeds and peanuts are easy snacks if he feels a panic attack building. A simple tea recipe of asafetida, nutmeg, cardamom, and ginger would also calm his mind. It can be made into a tea that he drinks throughout the day. Mint tea also is allowed, as well as chamomile tea.

She explains to us that there are certain foods he should avoid, including bitter foods, such as eggplant, mustard greens, arugula, and spinach. Black tea and coffee are forbidden. Chocolate is to be avoided. He should not eat any cheese, but especially goat cheese, which is considered "Rough and Light." Instead, Lobsang needs to eat nutritious foods, such as certain meats, stews, and food that is easy to digest.

Rough food is food that is hard to digest. Light food can be thought of as any stimulant that will affect and speed up the mind. This type of food is usually not very nutritious. The Tibetan concept of Rough and Light foods may be difficult to understand. *See Chapter 9 for an explanation of Rough and Light food.*

Moxibustion—Every time Lobsang visits the clinic, Dr. Jamling and I perform moxibustion on him, burning the herb *Artemisia vulgaris* on the front and back points of the body.

NOTE: *For more information on the moxibustion procedure, see Chapter 10.*

Aromatherapy—Dr. Jamling gives Lobsang a special *rLung* incense stick for him to burn at dawn and in the evening—the times of heightened *rLung* energy and anxiety. She shows him how to breathe it in. The theory behind incense aromatherapy is that the breath is intimately linked with the mind. By deeply breathing in the incense, the mind calms down. The special ingredients in the incense bring soothing herbs in minute quantities into the energetic channels where *rLung* resides.

Some of the ingredients of this incense recipe include: aloeswood, myrobalan, asofoetida, *Aquilaria*, and roseroot. The herbal pills contain the same herbal ingredients as in the incense, but in differing quantities and combinations. Dr. Jamling actually makes this special incense in her monastery in Dharamsala. It is made from a "secret" recipe from The Four Tantras, the main Tibetan medical text. For generations it has been used to ease the symptoms of *rLung* Imbalance.

NOTE: *See Resources for more information about ordering this special incense.*

Bodywork—For Lobsang, both his stomach and his heart are affected by the *rLung* Imbalance. Dr. Jamling recommends massaging the *rLung* points on both the front and back of the body to help with this kind of imbalance.

The warmed massage oil is a mixture of sesame oil, fennel seeds or star anise, caraway seeds, and nutmeg. Massage is an important part of the treatment, and Lobsang takes it upon himself to find someone to do the massage every day in the first weeks of treatment.

NOTE: *For information on rLung massage and the oil recipe, see Chapter 10.*

A Tibetan Healing Exercise to Help with *rLung*—Dr. Jamling recommends that Lobsang roll his head around completely three times in one direction, and three times in another, very slowly, every morning and evening after using the incense. This relaxes the shoulders and also facilitates the smooth flow of the life channel energy between the head and the heart. It also grounds him.

NOTE: *For information on Tibetan Healing exercises such as the Head Roll, see Chapter 11.*

Less Meditation, More Gentleness—Dr. Jamling instructs Lobsang as he listens intently, "There must be a gentleness toward your mind. It should not be strictly controlled, just watched. Meditation attempts to control the mind, and too much meditation can intensify the *rLung* Imbalance." He nods as she continues, "The medical texts recommend that monks with *rLung* Imbalance avoid thinking too much or sitting and meditating excessively." Dr. Jamling also tells him that she will talk to his abbott (the monastery leader) about slowing down his meditation practice until the *rLung* disturbance is resolved.

Over the next six weeks of treatment, I witnessed Lobsang blossom into a completely relaxed person, free from anxiety—a debilitating condition that affected every aspect of his life. We treated Lobsang once per week with moxibustion, and he received massage weekly from an assistant at the monastery. He followed our recommendations for dietary restrictions and refrained from meditating intensely. He appears happier and more encouraged as the weeks go on, and he seems almost relieved to be freed from the practice of intense meditation. Lobsang appears more grounded, less anxious, and he has put on some weight.

At the sixth clinical visit, his pulse has returned to normal, and he tells us that he has not had any anxiety or panic attacks in two and a half weeks. He still experiences some stomach gurgling and anxiety when hungry, but when he eats his warm soup, this disappears. Lobsang continued to check in with us over the next couple of months, and only comes to the clinic occasionally, as needed.

Lobsang has learned to manage his anxiety. He has stopped taking the special incense in the mornings, phasing it out almost completely until he no longer needs it except if he feels the uneasiness coming back. While he has a tendency for *rLung* disturbance and it could potentially return, Lobsang now knows how to manage his lifestyle to keep himself in balance. Success in Lobsang's case gives me great hope that these simple changes can give him, and others anywhere in the world, the quality of life they so desire. Cheers to Tashi Delek Lobsang!

Past, Present and Future

Dr. Jamling said to me, many years ago when visiting the United Sates, "There is so much *rLung* in your country, we need to write a book in English about *rLung!*" And she was right. Sixty percent of the patients in my practice in the United States suffer from anxiety.

Anxiety, stress, mental restlessness, even severe mental illness (which Tibetans call *srog-rLung*, pronounced sok-loong) affects millions of Americans. Anxiety disorders are the most common mental illnesses in the United Sates, affecting 40 million adults age 18 and older (or 18% of the United Sates population, as reported by the National Institute of Health).[2] Tibetan medical treatments for *rLung* could help solve this problem and bring down this statistic.

Tibetan medicine has a deep understanding of the mind-body connection and for centuries has documented successful treatments for *rLung* Imbalance. The primary reason for Tibetan Medicine's success with anxiety lies in its ability to understand the *chi* mechanism in the body–the vital force that cannot be seen. Tibetan medical doctors also can recognize three main constitutional types of people, and thus treatment is more holistic and tailor-made to each individual. Tibetan Medicine is successful with anxiety because it not only uses oral medicine (an herbal pill formula), but also applies diet, bodywork, and mental health practices (for example, meditation) to help develop healthy lifestyles leading to mental clarity and inner peace. In the future, I would like to see Tibetan medical treatments becoming the new standard for all mind-body illnesses.

Finding the Underlying Cause

When I was first being introduced to Tibetan Medicine through working with Dr. Jamling, she said to me:

> In Tibetan Medicine, two people can come into the clinic with, let's say, the same red rash on the arm. On the surface of the body, it looks like the same disease, but they may actually have very different underlying imbalances.

Upon hearing this, I realized that finding the underlying imbalances is crucial to solving an *rLung* Imbalance successfully. Each underlying pattern of imbalance involves differing amounts of the mind and body's energies. For example in biomedicine, a person may have what is just called "anxiety." In Tibetan Medicine, a person may have anxiety with an underlying imbalance of an organ system, or anxiety with an imbalance of one of the Three Humors: Wind (*rLung*), Bile (*Tipa*), or Phlegm (*Bad-Gan*). We will talk more about these Three Humors in *Chapter 6*.

When looking at any disease, we must first ask ourselves, "Where is the rLung?"
—Dr. Dadhon Jamling

Anxiety can stem from an imbalance of a particular constitutional body type or from a behavioral activity that is responsible for the disease, such as improper diet or continued overwork. A combination of any of these can cause a body to become imbalanced and start to break down, energetically speaking. In the United States and in other parts of the world, this way of living seems almost the norm. Needless to say, *rLung* Imbalance is running rampant and existing under the guise of being labeled simply "anxiety," leaving people to their own devices to figure out what to do for treatments, or not do anything at all.

Simple Changes in Lifestyle and Diet

The primary goal of Tibetan Medicine is to help people settle their minds and root themselves in a grounded lifestyle. Their healing advice is rooted in simplicity. In contrast to the actual sophistication of Tibetan medical knowledge, the remedies for mental imbalance, such as anxiety and sadness, or even depression, are simple, earthy, and enjoyable. While herbal medicine can be helpful, you must consult a Tibetan Medicine practitioner for a prescription. However, even without herbal pills, these simple techniques and recipes, such as dietary changes, meditation, acupressure, massage, and the *rLung* incense can be applied by anyone. This simple approach can be profoundly helpful in relieving, soothing, and calming most anxious and stressful thoughts. They are also inexpensive and ecological. The meditation techniques can easily become a lifelong learning tool for understanding oneself more deeply.

As a practitioner of Asian medicine in the United States, I work with many people who want to transition off anxiety medication, and I witness them emerging from their anxiety whole and complete, with the ability to feel more deeply than they did before. When I first meet them, they almost always appear to be addicted to their anxiety medication and experience various side effects, such as being overweight or suffering from insomnia. Many are still anxious despite taking the medication. As one woman said to me, "It took me two years to come off my anxiety medication. I still have deep-seated fears sometimes, but I also now have my life back. I have lost weight, and there is less of a wall of medication between me and the world...my social anxiety still rears its ugly head in certain situations... but I can handle it because I've learned the tools to deal with anxiety thanks to your guidance."

It is very impoortant to ask many questions on diet and lifestyle because these are the roots of disease, causing imbalance of the three humors. They are also the cure.
—Dr. Dadhon Jamling

When people follow the simple path of more wholesome habits, especially the calming of the mind through meditation, exercise, and diet, life is observed more clearly. People start to grow and evolve at a much faster pace than if they were continuing their lives with a muddy and agitated mind. The agitated mind takes up a lot of energy. By deepening our spiritual life, or whatever you want to call the path of Tibetan Medicine, we find lasting joy and happiness. The holistic approach of Tibetan Medicine for relieving anxiety and *rLung* Imbalance results in a stronger person, both mentally and physically.

My clients who come off their medication feel like they've accomplished much and have a deeper sense of themselves. They have successfully developed new healthy personal habits thanks to Tibetan Medicine and their own discipline and hard work. They are meditating, exercising more, using the Tibetan incense, and have new dietary habits that are more nourishing for their constitution. By eliminating or reducing their anxiety medication, they feel more aware of themselves and others. It is as if they feel more connected and involved in their lives, like the medication had buffered and separated them from the world around them. They feel more in contact with reality, exactly as things are. Many clients remark on how intensely joyous and wonderful life is, but also how intensely the struggle of life requires a new kind of courage for them. When working with anxiety medication, I always work closely with a person's doctor. Sometimes a person can only lessen the medication by milligrams. Even so, they still come away more aware and with healthy lifestyle tools that bring them closer to themselves, their inner self, their constitutional type, and ultimately, more confident and strong when facing their fears.

While the United Sates has mostly focused on making technological advances, such as electricity, the telephone, nuclear weapons, computers, and cell phones in the last hundred years, Tibetan Buddhist scholars have concentrated on making inner developmental advances for the last thousand years. Tibetan Buddhist monks have mapped out an inner psychology or roadmap of the mind and the way in which it is intertwined with the body. This mind/body connection also shows us how to prevent mental instability as well as how to heal ourselves when we do become mentally imbalanced.

This has been the foundation for great advances in our understanding of both consciousness and psychology—knowledge we are only now beginning to appreciate in the West.

Tibetan Medicine provides a more holistic approach to healing the cause of the symptoms, not just the symptoms themselves. What is unique about Tibetan Medicine is that its roots are in Buddhism. Buddhist monks found that by directing the flow of their *rLung*, or their vital force, they were able to feel calmer. Their minds were more at peace. It has been over two thousand years since Buddha walked the earth. The religious documents of those times describe his concrete practices for a calmer mind, which later grew into larger tractates that became recipes for treating mental health. Buddhist monks often acted as the doctors in their communities, and thus evolved one of the greatest medical systems in the world. We are only now just beginning to tap the knowledge Tibetan Medicine has of the treatment of psychosomatic illnesses.

The Existence and Importance of Suffering

The Buddhist medical texts state that all disease originates in the mind. A person's basic cravings, anger, and slothfulness of the mind can have a negative affect on their body. Since the root of all disease, and of all suffering, is the mind, Tibetan doctors always ask themselves first, "What is this patient's mood? How is the suffering expressed? Is it anger? Is it sluggishness? Is it constant worrying and craving for something different in life?" This suffering of the mind will affect each organ of the body differently, depending on its quality.

Dr. Jamling expressed an important distinction about suffering:

> In the West . . . suffering is seen as a bad thing . . . But this is not always so. Imbalance in the body/mind is not necessarily a negative thing. A Tibetan doctor may say to a patient that the actual mental afflictive state itself is fortunate, as it is a milestone of awareness that can help the patient more firmly put their foot on the path of enlightenment, the path to understanding the nature of their own mind.

In Tibetan Medicine, suffering is seen as an opportunity to discover more about oneself, to grow and expand one's consciousness. While attending a Buddhist gathering in a small temple courtyard in Northern India in 1997, a small and frail-looking Lama returning from the United States told an interesting story that has since made its way around Buddhist circles, with varying details:

> A medical doctor, a surgeon of known repute, was in a terrible car accident. His car was hit head-on by a drunk driver, and he swerved to the other side of the highway, flipping his car over twice, thus causing a monumental 16-car accident. The man's car landed in the ditch at the side of the highway. It took several hours to extricate him from the car. He was then rushed to the emergency room, suffering from a severe head wound that caused blindness in one eye. Both arms and legs

were broken, and he was rushed into surgery to place permanent pins in both arms and to extract metal from his right leg. Multiple bruises and injuries to internal organs meant that he had to stay in the hospital for over three weeks, until all his vital signs had stabilized. He was not married, but friends gathered every day and evening to attend to his needs. On the tenth day, his Buddhist teacher visited him and bent over him as he lay in traction on the bed. The venerable teacher shook his head vigorously back and forth, back and forth, and repeated to himself, "Lucky, lucky man!"

You may ask how anyone could look at that broken man in a hospital bed and say to him that he is a lucky man. But think about the reasoning of the Tibetan mind. The lama recounted that the Buddha described three kinds of suffering: 1) the suffering of pain, 2) the suffering of change, and 3) the suffering of conditionality, or conditioned, limited existence on earth. The lucky man from the story is indeed "lucky" because in one moment in time, the three kinds of suffering were made evident to him. This type of profound pain leads to what the Lama called, "The Clearing Field." This is where suddenly, all that seems important in one's life—reputation, possessions, good looks, youth—disappears, and the deeper meaning of life emerges, instantaneously, joyfully, and completely. It is this precious knowledge—greater than any material possession that was gained—that will never leave its master. It is an awareness that the lama says brings a certain "joy" unknown to the common man—hence the "lucky, lucky man" in the story.

Anxiety can make us suffer. It can also deepen our awareness and longing for serenity and peace. The tools in this book illuminate our awareness of ourselves. And there is nothing like the joy of regulating our *rLung* energy—it's like harnessing the wind!

We are what we think.

All that we are arises with our thoughts.
With our thoughts we make the world.

Speak or act with a pure mind,
And happiness will follow you.

Your worst enemy cannot harm you
As much as your thoughts, unguarded.

But once mastered,
No one can help you as much,
Not even your father or your mother.

—from the The Dhammapada,
a collection of sayings of the Buddha in verse form

FOUR

YANGCHEN'S IRE

When Yangchen comes in, she smiles broadly at both of us, and soon the clinic is filled with mirth and joy. There are warm exchanges about the children, the weather, and talk of the birth of Yangchen's third grandchild. Yangchen is a heavy-set woman, and she walks with a slight limp that makes her rock from side to side. Her face is weathered, and I am unable to place her age. Her black and gray hair is pulled back in a loose bun, and she wears a beautiful Tibetan *chupa* dress, with the embroidered front, indicating that she is married. Her hands appear gnarled and worn, perhaps with rheumatism.

We talk to Yangchen and find out she is 48 years old. She is married and has four children. She and her husband have a business making and selling sweaters to the tourists around Dharamsala. Yangchen's sisters also help with the knitting, and they have created a very successful small-cottage industry, running out of small living rooms throughout the area. Yangchen and her husband are very happy. They are both known around town for their dancing abilities, especially

Yangchen. Dr. Jamling tells me that when she was younger, Yangchen was a very good dancer, and she often performed spontaneously for everyone at family gatherings.

Yangchen's Anger and Shifting Pains

As Dr. Jamling starts to take her pulses, the laughter settles down. Yangchen looks worried. Primarily, she says, she has fits of anger. She explains that her strong fiery temperament has been an asset in the past. It has given her great courage to undertake many difficult tasks, such as traveling long distances to sell her sweaters on her own. However, nowadays, her fiery temperament is causing her stress. She feels a lot of pent up frustration and anger that she thinks has no real basis in her daily life: her children are settled, she and her husband get along well, and they have financial stability and a good life. So, why is she so frustrated? She believes her current problems are being caused by a *rLung* Imbalance and asks Dr. Jamling to prescribe some medicines.

Yangchen describes having pain in the nape of her neck, called the cervical plexus, which is the area around the first four cervical vertebrae. She also complains of a stitch in her side. These areas feel painful, particularly at dusk, which is one of the times of day when *rLung* can be more intense. She also suffers from frequent sighing, which seems to relieve some of the pressure in her chest. She has insomnia and tells us of pain in her hips and around her waist. Her joints hurt too, but mostly it seems to be related to the pain around her upper spine and neck. This pain can sometimes radiate down her arms. Yangchen describes the waist and hip pain as shooting pain, coming in bursts and passing quickly. Her stomach is also always gurgling, as if it takes a long time for her to digest anything. She informs us that even if she eats just a single cracker, her stomach will swell up as if she's had a huge meal. Her mouth also becomes very dry at times, and she is often unable to quench her thirst.

Of all the symptoms, the mental-emotional ones worry Yangchen most. She is irritable upon waking and has outbursts of anger that disturb her. Her hands shake sometimes when she is angry, and she can feel the pain in her neck intensify. She gets depressed sometimes, a kind of lethargy and sadness, but she says there really is no reason for it. She longs for the days when she was happy and more carefree.

Making a Diagnosis: Yangchen's Constitution

In Tibetan medical terms, the mind and body exist along an intertwined continuum, where the subtle functions of the mind, from conception all the way to birth, result in a physical body. Even the various fluids: blood, bile, and semen are the result of different aspects of consciousness coming into physical form.

In the clinic, when Tibetan medical doctors are diagnosing a patient, they are observing the patient's state of mind, and how it may be related to certain patterns of dysfunction in the body. Doctors collect information through the empirical evidence of pulse diagnosis, urine analysis, palpation, and patient interview. This is what makes Tibetan Medicine unique: this interplay between states of mind, and how they affect health and disease. The Buddha himself stated that a mind imbalance is the root of all disease. By tracing the roots of illness back to states of mind and patterns of bodily imbalance, healing happens on many levels: physical, mental, environmental, and through changes of habitual behavior.

Dr. Jamling takes Yangchen's pulse and confirms that it is fast and that it disappears when she presses harder, which is called a floating, empty pulse. She finds that the stomach pulse is weak,

Tongue diagnosis is used to assess the client's health

showing signs of deficiency, confirming that the digestion is weak. The tongue is very dry, without a coating, with some cracks, showing the intense dryness she must be experiencing as thirst. This is a typical *rLung* Imbalance

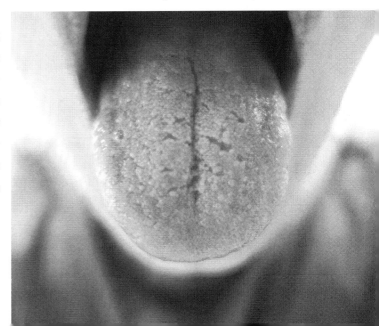

tongue presentation: it is dry, with very little coating, and somewhat red underneath.

According to Tibetan Medicine, in the human body there are dynamic forces continuously interacting, every moment. If these fundamental forces are in equilibrium, we are healthy. The three main forces in the body are called the three humors: Wind (*rLung*), Bile (*Tipa*), and Phlegm (*Bad-Gan*), which are covered in Chapter 6. If one of the humors is depleted, or in excess, it affects the other humors, and a disease process, perhaps subtle at first, unfolds.

When assessing a tongue for *rLung* Imbalance, look for any of the following:

- A dry tongue (very little moisture or glistening on top of the tongue)
- Little coating (not covered with a white or yellow color) or a peeled coating (a coat that has patches "peeled off" or areas where there is no coat)
- A little too red (tongues are normally pinkish/red, this is a brighter than normal red)
- A crack down the middle

Yangchen's constitution tends toward *Tipa*, which means there could be a liver imbalance, which would explain the quick outbursts of anger. When *rLung* and *Tipa* combine, the patient will tend toward frustration and outbursts of anger in the beginning, then the *rLung* will enter the stomach, causing digestive issues. Dr. Jamling notices Yangchen's eyes are red, which is typical when there is *Tipa* involvement in the *rLung* disturbance. Dr. Jamling also examines her urine, which she finds to be clear, watery, and tinged with blue—typical of *rLung* Imbalances.

To understand the underlying causes of her condition, Dr. Jamling asks Yangchen about her childbirth history. Yangchen tells us that her last child had a very long and difficult birth, resulting in the loss of a lot of blood. Dr. Jamling asks if the *rLung* symptoms started after that childbirth, and Yangchen confirms that they did. Dr. Jamling explains to Yangchen that there can be an underlying depletion from the childbirth, even from many years ago, that makes Yangchen more susceptible to *rLung* disturbance. Once *rLung* has been disturbed, it can happen again, becoming an underlying chronic illness.

Dr. Jamling describes the type of *rLung* disturbance that Yangchen has:

> When *rLung* increases in the places where it resides, the smallest of life's disturbances can cause emotional imbalance, explosions, and also severe anxiety. There is a restlessness to the basic energy of the body . . .

Treatment

Dr. Jamling explains, as with most *rLung* patients, the most important goal of treatment is to pacify *rLung*, and settle it into the places in the body it normally resides. To minimize the activity of Yangchen's *rLung*, Dr. Jamling wants to focus on diet, massage, and undertaking moxibustion once per week in the clinic.

TIBETAN WALKING THERAPY

Dr. Jamling advises Yangchen to bring more exercise into her daily life, so that the *rLung* energy can flow freely, moving in a smooth manner through the channels. She suggests to her that she do spiritual practice walks, chanting the Medicine Buddha prayer for the health of all beings, while walking around the Tibetan Buddhist temple in the center of town, spinning the wheels that send blessings out into the world. By doing this twice a day, Yangchen is guaranteed to feel her breathing become deeper and more relaxed.

MOXIBUSTION

We undertake her first course of moxibustion in the clinic. Closely following the instructions of the *rGyud-bzhi*, we warm the points on the back of the neck and the lower lumbar region. Dr. Jamling uses sesame oil for this. Then she applies the moxibustion to the *nadis/* acu-points for *rLung*, on the front and back of the body. This in itself relaxes Yangchen immediately. We are settling the *rLung* back into its proper channels. Her breathing improves, and the stitch in her side clears up within minutes. Dr. Jamling asks Yangchen to come in once a week for moxibustion. She agrees.

DIET

Dr. Jamling tells Yangchen that the most important thing of all is to cut down her intake of black tea and to eat nutritious foods that settle the *rLung*, thus nourishing the body. The basic *rLung* diet consists of oily, nutritious food. It should include protein that is warm, soft, and has a "mushy" consistency, such as eggs, nut butters, and cheese. Soups and stews with grains and root vegetables are also helpful. These foods help to nourish and moisturize the body, lubricate the muscles and sinews, and maintain warmth. They also help with elimination and digestion. Yangchen is also advised to avoid heat-producing spicy foods in order to dampen her *Tipa* constitution. (The heat in spicy food can dry up the fluids in her body.) She is told to avoid lamb, which is a meat that creates a lot of heat.

HERBAL MEDICINE

In the beginning, Dr. Jamling gives Yangchen a prescription of herbal pills, Eaglewood 35, to facilitate recovery from this type of *rLung* disease. She is to take them in the morning and at night. While the herbal pills will be helpful, this condition could also be treated with just dietary changes, moxibustion, and special *rLung* incense. *See Resources for more information about these herbal pills.*

Back to Her Old Self

In four weeks, Yangchen's insomnia has cleared up, and the pressure in her chest has disappeared. The outbursts of anger have also lessened. Dr. Jamling stops the use of herbal pills, and instructs Yangchen to continue with being mindful with her diet, and to continue her walks around the village temple twice a day.

In six weeks, Yangchen feels she is back to her old self, and all of her symptoms have disappeared. Her husband accompanies her into the clinic on her last scheduled visit to personally thank Dr. Jamling for helping his wife get back to her happy ways. Periodically, Yangchen comes into the clinic, when her lifestyle and diet have gone awry, and her symptoms of anger and stress appear again. She is reminded what to do to bring herself back on course, through diet and lifestyle, and the *rLung* is kept under control. Yangchen is pleased to be back to her old ways of being very social, enjoying her grandchildren, and dancing again through life!

Three Humors and Five Elements

The Three Humors and the theory of the Five Elements constitute the basis of Tibetan medical diagnosis and treatment. The theory of the Five Elements is common to both Chinese and Tibetan Medicine, but should not be confused, as there are many fundamental differences. In Tibetan Medicine, the Five Elements are: Earth, Water, Fire, Air, and Space. The body's development as a fetus begins when the mind stream of the soul differentiates into characteristic energies, called the Five Elements. The Five Elements begin as the Five Lights: the gentlest differentiation of consciousness, expressing itself in color and an associated primary emotion. One cannot, in fact, be born without this differentiation of energies, or of consciousness, that is taking place inside. The seed of consciousness becomes the Five Lights, and they coalesce to ultimately create physical form, but the consciousness is present in every facet of the human form.

All living creatures consist of their own specific combination of the Three Humors and Five Elements. As humans, this is what makes each of us unique. When a fetus develops, one of the Five Elements will be more dominantly expressed than another. The Three Humors and Five Elements shape, for example, the body type and what interests a person, or whether they are an extrovert or introvert. They reveal the basic temperament of a person, such as whether they are prone to anger, despondency, or worry, and what type of mental illness a given person may be prey to.

The Three Humors and the theory of the Five Elements constitute the basis of Tibetan medical diagnosis and treatment.

Many combinations of the Three Humors and Five Elements are possible, so Tibetan doctors categorize patients into different constitutional types. This allows them to determine treatment strategies, offering differing diet and behavioral treatment for each type. In Tibetan Medicine there are no blanket statements about how red meat is good for everyone, or everyone should eat raw vegetables. Instead, the constitutional types require certain amounts of meat or vegetables, cold or warm environments, isolation from large crowds, or even constant, intense attention and affection—all depending upon the expression of the Three Humors and Five Elements. The goal in Tibetan Medicine is to find a balance that works for each type. *Chapter 9* will go into greater detail about understanding the effects of the Three Humors and Five Elements on diet.

MIND, EMOTION, AND OUR UNIQUE CONSTITUTION

The physiology of the body in Tibetan Medicine begins with the Three Humors, or what Tibetan doctors explain as the "three mental poisons," of ignorance, anger, and desire. How is it that the Three Humors are referred to as the three negative emotions and mental poisons? In Tibetan medical texts, and in Buddhist psychological treatises, Buddha traced the origin of all suffering to one basic desire or urge, which then branched into these three fundamental emotions. To even be born, it is said in the Buddhist scriptures, a fundamental desire is necessary. The result of this desire is a human birth. This fundamental desire is an attachment to something, an inability to let go of an interest from before one was born. Instead of resting in the pure awareness of the Absolute, beyond space and time, there is an urge. There are challenges that the unborn soul wants to work out, a kind of basic clinging and affliction, or on a more concrete level in earthly terms, unresolved issues with people and places where one is to be born. This can be thought of as karma or the result of previous actions or lifetimes.

To be born, it is said in the Buddhist scriptures, a fundamental desire is necessary.

Buddha called this basic desire *bDag-zin* (pronounced dag-zin), which means ego. This ego further differentiates into three basic emotions. Each of the three basic emotions give rise to a particular humor. Here again in Tibetan Buddhist medicine, we see that mind, emotion, and physical existence are always inextricably intertwined. This fundamental attachment of the unborn, or soon to be born, soul results in the manifestation of a physical reality as a fetus. The fetus could not ultimately be born unless this extreme, focused push of desire crystallized into the strong will of physical form. In Tibetan Medicine, this is where it all begins. Of the three basic emotions, ignorance is associated with the humor Phlegm, anger is associated with Bile, and desire is associated with Wind.

In Tibetan Buddhist medicine, we see that mind, emotion, and physical existence are always inextricably intertwined.

When the humors and emotions are in equilibrium, the body functions normally and carries out its tasks in life, governed by the will of an individual consciousness. In great health, the three humors are in balance, and there is an exuberance of will to undertake the tasks that are encountered in life. When disease results from various causes, there are characteristic states of mind that doctors can trace back to an imbalance of a particular humor or bodily function associated with the humor.

The combinations of *rLung* and *Bad-Gan* or *rLung* and *Tipa* will result in very different symptoms. By considering each of these forces as responsible for certain emotional and bodily functions, a Tibetan doctor can tease apart wherein the imbalances lie. Treatment principles will involve bringing these same forces back into control or back into balance.

Negative states of mind can in fact result in disease. I personally believe this is one main reason that the stigma of mental illness is much milder in Tibetan society. The mentally ill are seen more as victims of some bodily imbalance, and they are not blamed for their mental health issues as they sometimes are in other parts of the world.

If there is one thing I know that Tibetan Medicine can offer the West, it is our understanding of mental health.

— *Dr. (Lady) Dadhon Jamling*

FIVE

HEALING THE HURRIED CHILD: ANNABELLA'S STRESSFUL LIFE

After finishing graduate school, I lived in Denmark, where I studied and practiced acupuncture. During that time, I continued to return to Dharamsala for my postdoctoral work. However, with each passing year, my personal life began to interfere more and more with my work. I married and began a family. I moved back to the United Sates, where I grew up, with my family in tow, and the responsibilities of children and life in the West took hold.

Bringing Tibetan Medicine Home

When I had first started down my career path, I thought I would be doing some form of aid organization work, such as bringing biomedicine abroad and continuing to improve the health and lives of refugees. However, as fate would turn, I had discovered Tibetan Medicine and my career path shifted as I became completely absorbed in it. I knew I could still do much good in the world, just perhaps on a smaller scale. There was nothing really for me to "help" with as a biomedically trained medical anthropologist in Dharamsala. The Tibetans were taking quite good care of themselves. Instead I realized

opposite:
Dr. Ryan in her Greenfield, MA herbal apothecary

that we in the West had so much to learn from Tibetans. I eventually decided to leave my aid organization work behind, but not my love and respect for the Tibetan people (they will remain forever in my heart) and Tibetan Medicine.

After a short stint as a professor in medical anthropology, I felt a pull in a new direction, both emotionally and intellectually. I realized I didn't want to write for medical journals touting Tibetan Medicine, but I wanted to go out and practice it and help individuals directly. I chose to finish my training in Asian Herbal Medicine with the desire to open an herbal apothecary. I focused on using herbal medicine, acupressure, moxibustion, and Tibetan medical dietary advice to alleviate anxiety and depression. I included mind training and relaxation techniques from Tibetan Buddhist scriptures that I had learned in my years in Dharamsala.

Initially, it took some time and research to figure out how to apply these theories to help individuals from a completely different culture. But I was determined, and with the support of my family and friends, I soon had a busy practice with many lives being improved daily. It continues to surprise me how simply the Tibetan approach can be applied to someone's life and how helpful it has been to my community. Thanks to Tibetan healing theories, the growing number of teenagers and adults now walking around my hometown without anti-depressants (and their ill side effects), instills and inspires in me the hope that spreading this information can continue to help improve the lives of others in the United States and all over the world, which is the driving force of this book. I love sharing and educating people of the joys and happiness of life through simple, yet effective, healing treatments.

Annabella's Paralyzing Fear

Annabella is 11 years old. She comes to my clinic in Massachusetts with her mother, Tricia. Annabella is slight for her age, wiry, and appears strong. She takes ballet lessons five times per week and has violin practice on Saturdays. She attends one of the best private schools in our area and gets very good academic grades. When she comes in, I immediately notice how she walks closely behind her mother, holding her hand, as if she were in a frightened state. She sat down very close to her mother and gave me a furtive and almost distrustful glance. Tricia, her mother, did all the talking.

Thank you so much for seeing us! I am just desperate. Our psychiatrist told me that you may be able to help us . . . Annabella just isn't herself anymore. I don't understand it. Until two months ago, she was an energetic, happy-go-lucky child with absolutely no fears or problems whatsoever . . . and then . . . I cannot bear the thought of her on any medication. So I thought we would try herbal medicine approaches first.

I nod and continue to listen to her story.

. . . She developed what she calls this strange muzziness in her head. It was so embarrassing! We were at a birthday party. She didn't know what day it was, or what we had planned to do that day. Now she has so many irrational fears; I don't know where to begin. The closet doors around the house always have to be shut; books need to be in a certain order; when the wind blows, she is frightened that the trees will fall on the house. Her anxiety is the worst at night, and I have to lie with her until she falls asleep. Also, she needs to urinate frequently. It's as if this calms her down. Sometimes, to me, she sounds . . . well, like she needs serious help. Other times, it's as if she has just regressed a few years.

When I turn to Annabella, she is not looking at me. It is clear to me that it is going to take some time before she trusts me. For the first session, we just chat easily and try to get to know one another better. I do a detailed intake of Annabella's life, and the following symptoms come to light.

The Perfect Child

Annabella's lifestyle clearly has exacerbated her symptoms. With the pressures of being at an advanced academic school with much of her time committed to daily homework, ballet lessons, and violin lessons—along with irregular meals—Annabella's *rLung* symptoms have been steadily increasing.

Annabella experiences a compressed feeling in her head as if everything is pressing into her—a feeling of being taken over by "something in her brain" without her being able to control it. She feels as if she is locked inside herself. The fuzziness in her head, as she calls it, is "more like there is so much going on in there, that I can't pick out what is the most important thing in this very second . . . "

The mental confusion and compressed feeling in her head appears to be exacerbated by her busy schedule. With the intense athletic and mental focus required by her ballet classes, she is exhausted by dinner time. This is when her hysteria begins to build and get stronger. It is definitely worse before eating. Her mother has begun to have a thermos of hot stew ready for her, right away after ballet class, and this seems to help with Annabella's mood.

Annabella also complains of gnawing hunger that is uncomfortable and a constant urge to eat warm foods. She and her family are vegetarian, and unfortunately, due to all of their busy schedules, they eat a lot of take-out food: greasy Indian curries one night, Chinese food the next, and sushi the following. The gnawing hunger in her stomach is worse in the evening and upon waking up in the morning.

The location of the anxiety, hysteria, and fear is in her heart and lung area, but she also tells me when feeling great fear, she needs to move her hands agitatedly, fidgeting and sometimes is compelled to get up to walk around. She says this anxiety occurs, "nearly all the time."

Her tongue is red, peeled, and there is a central crack. It is rare for one so young to have a central crack on the tongue. This shows that her constitution has a proclivity for *rLung* Imbalance.

Annabella tells me that she also has a lot of stomach gas and dry, hard stools. When *rLung* affects the intestines, it makes the stool dry with a consistency of rabbit pellets. She is also not drinking enough during the day.

I ask Annabella if she had experienced any type of shock that devastated her. She answers:

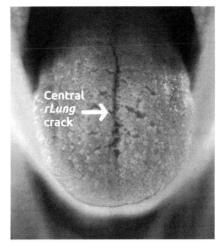

Well, yeah... a very strange thing happened. One day at my violin lesson, my teacher really yelled at me. I hadn't practiced, and I was tired, and sort of spacing out. She really yelled at me loudly. My mom and dad don't yell, so I was kind of shocked. It was the first time that this ever happened to me... At the end of the lesson, I ran downstairs to my mom crying. She was upset to see me like that, and the violin teacher didn't mention the yelling but told my mom that she was frustrated with my lack of practicing. My mom believed me that my teacher had yelled and stuck up for me when I told her... and so now I have a new teacher.

Tongue showing central *rLung* crack

I nod as I continue to write her notes down.

Her busy lifestyle requires eating food on the run every day that is of a rough and light quality—no meat, lots of vegetables and rice, cooked in restaurants and eaten haphazardly. This diet also exacerbates and increases her natural predisposition toward *rLung* disturbance. The crack in the middle of her tongue, extending all the way to the tip, is rare for children. Typically when a child has such a crack, it could indicate a constitutional predisposition to *rLung* Imbalance. She may have a congenital weakness in the family that contributes to her mental imbalance.

Annabella exhibits the typical *rLung* constitution, meaning the *rLung* humor is predominant. With Annabella, the shock and the mental confusion means that the all-pervading *rLung* has been disturbed.

The Tibetan medical text says that when the all-pervading *rLung* is disturbed, there has often been a shock or great trauma to the system, with accompanying symptoms of anxiety, irrational fears, and mental confusion (in her case, a "muzzy head" and an inability to understand time).

Less is More for Annabella

My goal for working with Annabella is to pacify *rLung* and settle it back into its natural places. With such a young person, this can be done through diet, behavioral changes, using Dr. Jamling's special *rLung* incense, and moxibustion on a regular basis. I do not recommend meditation or any extra activities for Annabella because of her clear need for spaciousness: more free time and fewer obligations.

FOOD FOR THE SOUL

I spoke with Annabella's mother about giving her small nutritious meals at regular hours. Her mother says she's willing to add high quality beef to her stews. I also recommend the herb fennel to help with her constipation, as fennel is an amazing herb that soothes the flow of *rLung* through the body's intestines. Her previous diet choice of white rice that has a light quality is replaced with brown rice for more nutrition. In the morning she eats steel-cut, organic oats in a simple boiled water sauce with a bit of butter. Annabella said she would prefer to limit the amount of meat in her diet, so I suggest her mother add mung beans and adzuki beans to be mixed with brown rice. I suggested replacing the acidic spinach with nutritious, *rLung* pacifying nettles to help with calming the *rLung* and providing a slight diuretic to soothe her bladder and to help her digestive system relax. I also suggest an increase in her intake of healthy snacks. Between regular meals, she can eat cashews, almonds, peanuts, and chestnuts to give her quick,

The Tibetan medical text says that when the all-pervading rLung is disturbed, there has often been a shock or great trauma to the system, with accompanying symptoms of anxiety, irrational fears, and mental confusion.

nutritious energy on busy days. She also agrees to cut out potato chips, candy, and sweets.

GENTLY REDUCING HER STRESS

For three weeks, Annabella's new direction consists of cutting down her time spent on ballet lessons from five times per week to two times per week. Violin lessons are reduced to every other week. She agrees to regular bedtimes without protest. We actually write down and map out her schedule to help consolidate her thoughts. I suggest she increase her outdoor exercising to get some fresh air and that she find quiet, restful play with friends with no overtly pressured social gatherings in the near future. She agrees to these changes, and her mother almost seems relieved that we are making a new plan for Annabella.

MASSAGE AND MOXA LESSONS FOR ANNABELLA'S MOTHER

Once a week in the clinic, moxibustion is done on the *rLung* stomach points and on the back points, over a period of three weeks. Annabella's mother is open to learning how to do the moxibustion at home with easy-to-use, stick-on moxa cones that I give her. This enables Annabella to receive moxibustion every night for three weeks at home on the newly learned points.

Annabella's mother also learns how to massage Annabella with a special oil I give her, massaging Annabella's back, stomach, and limbs before bed each night after doing the moxibustion. Any parent can learn these techniques. *For instructions on the basic massage oil recipe, see Chapter 10. See Chapter 12 for information about Moxibustion.*

ANNABELLA'S HUMOR RETURNS

The results of treatment with Annabella come about incrementally but steadily. Focusing on diet and behavior has a more gradual recovery period, which I explain to both Annabella and her mother so they can know what to expect. After six weeks, Annabella's humor returns. She is sleeping better at night. She has completely let go of her fears about falling trees and the closing of all the doors in the house and is now able to clearly plan her day without anxiety. I keep seeing Annabella for 12 weeks in total for treatment. By the end of these 12 weeks, Annabella is free of any *rLung* Imbalance symptoms. It is a delight to witness her transformation back to her true self.

Comparing the Case Histories

Each case history in this book has been selected to give you a different set of *rLung* Imbalance symptoms. Each person clearly suffered from more than one of the symptoms of *rLung* Imbalance as described by Dr. Jamling. From a healing perspective, this is true for almost every person suffering from anxiety, excessive stress, or PTSD. Each disorder manifests in a unique way and thus requires distinctive treatments and personalized remedies to restore *rLung* to its rightful condition and place. Each person's behavior and also constitution are different, so the treatments should be tailored to their specific needs.

For this reason, it's extremely important to delve into an individual's past and present in order to find out what specifically is causing his or her symptoms in order to treat each person uniquely. This way of diagnosis clearly opposes the principles of Western medicine, whereby doctors attempt to match patients' problems to predetermined sets of diagnoses and treatments.

Stewart's case history is more common among spiritual seekers who dabble in drinking alcohol and experiment with taking drugs. Stewart's situation was exacerbated by his poor diet, most likely from years prior. His case study shows us the extreme seriousness of when *rLung* gets severely out of balance.

My personal case history is an example of how overworking and poor diet can lead to more mild *rLung* Imbalance symptoms. What's significant about my experience of getting *rLung* Imbalance is that I learned how to keep my anxiety, insomnia, and stress at bay for over 25 years. Through a program of daily meditation and healthy diet, along with monitoring my workload so as to ensure that my workaholism doesn't get out of control, I have been stress free despite my constitutional propensity for *rLung* issues.

Lobsang's case history is important to examine because we can see that the *rLung* illness is due to a combination of his post traumatic stress from having fled his home on foot, his overwork at the monastery, and the daily stress and worry of making a new home in a foreign land. His story shows how the stress of overwork and striving to fit into a new culture can easily result in *rLung* illness.

Yangchen's *rLung* illness is of a different nature, most likely instigated by loss of blood and trauma of a long childbirth. Her case illustrates what happens when the body has a loss of blood and the basic temperament brings about a strong liver involvement: outbursts of anger, impatience, and the traveling pain so typical of *rLung* Imbalance will follow.

Annabella's case history is significant because her type of *rLung* Imbalance is commonly seen in our Western culture: an over-scheduled and improperly fed child overwhelmed by the pressures of performing in this modern life. Her *rLung* illness was more typical of what I've seen in my clinic on a daily basis in the United States. I have seen many children and young adults with varying *rLung* Imbalance symptoms. It is my hope that in the future, instead of defaulting to taking pharmaceuticals, children with anxiety can be helped through the use of simple advice on diet, lifestyle, mindfulness, massage, and moxibustion, since these methods can be administered so easily and done at home.

> It's extremely important to delve into an individual's past and present in order to find out what specifically is causing his or her symptoms in order to treat each person uniquely. This way of diagnosis clearly opposes the principles of Western medicine, whereby doctors attempt to match patients' problems to predetermined sets of diagnoses and treatments.

When the Iron Bird Flies and Horses Run on Wheels,
the Tibetan people will be scattered like ants
across the face of the earth,
and the teachings will come to the land
of the Red Faced People.

—*Padmasambhava, Guru Rinpoche of Tibet,*
8th Century

PART II OF HEALING ANXIETY GIVES YOU AN overview of what *rLung* is and how to understand it as an elemental force in the body that affects different organ systems. You will learn what the healthy purpose of *rLung* is, and also what happens when it goes awry.

Chapter 6 gives you an overview of the Three Humors in Tibetan Medicine: *rLung* (Wind), *Tipa* (Bile), and *Bad-Gan* (Phlegm). You will learn the physical and personality characteristics of the Three Humors so you can discover your own constitutional type to know yourself better and maintain health according to your own constitutional makeup.

The remaining chapters in Part II provide information about the specific Tibetan Medicine techniques you can use to get *rLung* back into balance. These powerful techniques include: Meditations, Diet, Massage, Healing Exercises, and Moxibustion.

PART II
FOUNDATIONS OF TIBETAN MEDICINE:
PUTTING THEORY
INTO PRACTICE

When I see a patient with a chronic illness,
I ask myself three questions:
where is the *rLung*?
what is their constitutional type, and also
what is their digestion like?
Chronic illness of any sort usually has
digestive issues over many years, and *rLung* . . .
Of course, seasonal considerations,
    and other factors are important,
but these three questions are the most important.

—Dr. (Lady) Dadhon Jamling

SIX

THE THREE HUMORS:
DISCOVER YOUR CONSTITUTION

Everyone is unique, and everyone has differing amounts of the Three Humors, according to Tibetan Medicine. The Three Humors are: *rLung* (Wind), *Tipa* (Bile), and *Bad-Gan* (Phlegm). You can understand a person's constitution through the Three Humors. For example, people who have *rLung* prominently in their constitutional makeup are more prone to *rLung* types of diseases. You can also look at how a person's particular illness relates to a particular humor. In the case of Yangchen—the mother and dancer— who was suffering from a *rLung* disease even though her frustration and anger relates to her basic *Tipa* constitutional type, you combine these symptoms and make a unique treatment that addresses both conditions.

Pure constitutional types are rarely seen in isolation from a mixture of one or more other humors. In other words, it's rare that a person is just one type of humor. Also, each humor has five energy types. This chapter describes each humor type in great detail so you can get a better understanding of the nuances of each type. Then it becomes easier

opposite:
Three patients waiting outside Dr. Jamling's clinic.

69

to blend the humors and see how one person may be a combination of two humors, such as a typical *rLung* type with some *Tipa* mixed in.

I. *Tipa*: Bile

Tipa (pronounced teepa) in Tibetan means flame. Traditionally, it is translated as Bile, but this should not be confused with the substance bile produced by the liver, although this substance is related to this humor.

The basic underlying emotion associated with Bile is anger. Bile is thus a motivating emotional force in our nature, giving us courage and fortitude in the face of difficulty, determination, and ambition. It is movement, will, and focus. So if this force of fortitude and courage is lacking in an individual, Tibetan doctors will question how Bile has contributed to a given disease pattern.

The telltale characteristics of people whose constitution is primarily Bile are:

- The body is usually of a **medium build**, not thin and not fat.
- They have a **proportionally pleasant appearance** (limbs, hands, feet in good proportions, and general appearance is pleasant).
- They can be **impatient and proud** people.
- They can also lean toward **obsessive-compulsive** behavior.
- They enjoy a good **challenge** and will work on something until they have mastered it.
- They are known for their **intelligence** but also for their jealousy.
- Their primary emotion is **anger**, but this does not necessarily mean they are angry people. In a healthy Bile person, it means they are **assertive** and can reach their goals. In imbalance, the anger can take over and riddle their system with toxins that lead to disease.
- They may express incredible **courage**, vitality, and ambition.
- They want to **solve problems** quickly and want to be the leaders in doing so. (You won't find a Bile type sitting around complaining about a problem.)

- They are generally **thirsty** and have a pronounced need to drink throughout the day.
- They are also often **hungry**, and when they are hungry it is urgent that they eat. It affects their mood severely if they cannot satisfy their hunger right away.
- They tend to have very **good blood circulation**.
- They tend to have **strong digestive heat**, so that they easily digest most foods. They can tend toward chronic diarrhea if unbalanced.
- They have an **oily complexion**.
- Their sweat has a very **strong odor**.
- They can **sweat** a lot.
- The men can tend toward becoming **bald** or **gray** early.
- They tend to **sleep well**, having no trouble falling asleep and having no trouble with getting up in the morning.

Spotting a *Tipa* Person:

Tipa people are high-achievers, outdoorsy, athletic, domineering, risk-takers. They like to get up early and scramble out the door right away. They talk a mile a minute, faster than anyone else. They could run a marathon by 10:00 a.m. When they get hungry, they need snacks immediately, or they get angry. They like spicy foods even though spice is bad for them.

Bile has specific pathways throughout the body. It moves through the sweat, is energetically housed in the eyes, liver, gall bladder, and intestines. Bile is responsible for the digestion of food through keeping the stomach's digestive fire warm and acidic. It provides warmth throughout the whole body and gives the ruddiness to our cheeks. It also has the quality of greasiness and lubricates the sinews and tendons, nourishing them. It is also responsible for our skin's complexion as well as our blood's purity, quality, color, and nutrient value.

If a disease is primarily Bile related, the eyes will take on a yellow or reddish appearance.

1. Accomplishing Bile

Accomplishing Bile is located in the heart and is responsible for:

- Our motivation to get out of bed in the morning.
- Our desire to achieve life goals and face difficulties with courage and stamina.
- Our confidence and focus on personal goals and incremental improvement of ourselves.
- An imbalance in this aspect of Bile is related to the type of depression that brings about an absolute inability to get out of bed.

2. Digestive Bile

Digestive Bile is located throughout the small intestine and part of the stomach and is responsible for:

- Digestion of food and liquids.
- Keeping the stomach and intestines warm and able to "rot" the food, as the Tibetan medical texts mention. Heat is needed for the digestion of food.

3. Color-Producing Bile

Color-Producing Bile is located in the liver and is responsible for:

- The maintenance, richness, and color of the blood.
- The nourishment of the muscles through the enrichment of nutrients obtained from digestion.
- Blood deficiency, such as iron deficiency, can be related to a imbalance in this aspect of Bile.

4. Complexion-Clearing Bile

Complexion-Clearing Bile is located in the pores of the skin. If you have a good complexion and do not suffer from acne, you have good Complexion Bile.

Complexion-Clearing Bile is responsible for:

- Ruddy cheeks in children.

- The color of our skin, the health of our moles, the quality of the hair on our skin, etc.
- Clearing toxins from our skin.

5. Bile of Sight

Bile of Sight is located in the liver and is responsible for:
- Our vision and anything related to the eyes.
- Eye problems are often related to an imbalance of this Bile (or Bile in general).
- Symptoms that show up in the eyes.
- The yellowing of the eyes is related to a disturbance in the Bile humor. Illnesses—such as hepatitis—are related to this aspect of Bile and often indicate problems with the liver and the gallbladder, which are said to "manifest in the eyes."

II. *Bad-Gan*: Phlegm

Bad-Gan (pronounced ba-gan) in Tibetan means Phlegm. It is the primary force in the body responsible for the production of cold and for slowing metabolic processes. It is known for lubricating and supporting the joints. It is the force that helps us to fall asleep—and stay asleep—and provides stability to our mind and emotions.

Phlegm can be visualized as the force within us that provides a settled feeling. The basic underlying emotion associated with *Bad-Gan* is ignorance. When imbalanced, it feels like sluggishness; when balanced, it's a feeling of repletion. On a physical level, Phlegm soothes, moisturizes, and lubricates.

The telltale characteristics of people whose constitutions are primarily Phlegm are:
- Great **patience and serenity** when needed.
- Unflappable **devotion** to others by nature.
- **Groundedness**.
- The **ability to sleep** through the night.
- A **rhythm to work**, plodding onward.

- The willingness to **carry through tasks** without any complaining.
- A **stable mind**.

Phlegm is located in the upper part of the body, especially the head, and the brain. It also permeates the flesh, fat, bones, marrow (which contains fat), regenerative fluid, excrement, urine, nose, tongue, lungs, spleen, stomach, urinary system, and kidneys. It is very closely associated with the forces of cold and water or wetness in the body and is found in nearly all bodily processes.

When a person's stability of mind becomes stagnant, and there is an excess of Phlegm, it results in heaviness—a sluggishness of mind. If you have an excess of Phlegm, it is common that you wake up with the feeling of fogginess in your head. When you eat a diet that is overly saturated with Phlegm foods, such as cheese, dairy, and carbohydrates, you may develop sluggishness upon awaking and laziness related to your thinking processes.

Spotting a *Bad-Gan* person:

Bad-Gan people are unflappable, hard but slow working, highly intelligent, good with people but introverted, and sensual. They let things roll off their back and don't let anyone get to them. They really enjoy their food and can struggle with their weight. They prefer intellectual tasks at their desk and humor is very important to them. Their skin is cool to the touch, and they are cuddly huggers. They sleep very soundly and love taking baths. They are the people you call to ask for advice and support.

THE FIVE TYPES OF PHLEGM

1. Supportive Phlegm

Supportive Phlegm is located in the chest and is the foundation for all the other Phlegm energies. It is responsible for the management of water in the body.

2. Connecting Phlegm

Connecting Phlegm is located in all the joints of the body and is responsible for:

- Movement in the body that involves joints.
- The flexibility of stretching.
- The swelling of the joints and pain in the joints. Especially in the elderly, this is related to a decrease of Connecting Phlegm in the body.

3. Satisfying Phlegm

The Satisfying Phlegm force is connected to all five sense organs and is located in the head and chest. It is responsible for:

- Connecting the sensations of seeing, hearing, smelling, tasting, and feeling to ourselves.
- Vertigo, when there is a disturbance of Satisfying Phlegm.
- Blurred vision, when there is a disturbance of Satisfying Phlegm.
- A sensation of fullness in the ears, related to an imbalance of Satisfying Phlegm.

4. Experiencing Phlegm

Experiencing Phlegm is located on the tongue and is responsible for all our sensations of taste.

5. Mixing Phlegm

Mixing Phlegm is located in the upper part of the digestive tract and is responsible for the digestion of food (with the help of Bile). Imbalances in Mixing Phlegm can cause:

- Bloating or a bloated feeling in the stomach, which can be due to a disturbance in Mixing Phlegm.
- Belching and the improper assimilation of food, which is related to an imbalance in Mixing Phlegm.
- Complex digestive disorders, such as chronic reflux, which are related to a weakness in both Mixing Phlegm and Supporting Phlegm.

III. *rLung*: Wind

When literally translated, *rLung* means movement. It is also translated as Wind. In keeping with previous English language texts, we refer to this humor interchangeably as *rLung* or Wind. We refer to the disease as *rLung* Disease or *rLung* Imbalance to distinguish the two uses of the word. Wind is associated with the emotion of desire, which helps to develop an idea, cling to it, and bring it to fruition.

The telltale characteristics of people whose constitutions are primarily *rLung* are:

- A **thin**, **short**, **wiry**, body type.
- A bluish or **dark complexion**.
- A **blue hue** to the lips.
- **Cracking sounds** in the joints.
- **Highly intelligent**.
- A **quick wit**.
- Fond of **laughing** and arguing.
- **Ability to concentrate** on many things at one time.
- Prone to **not finishing tasks** and flitting from one idea to another.
- **Spreading themselves too thin** when there is an imbalance in *rLung*.

Spotting a *rLung* person:

A *rLung* person tends to be on the skinny side, nervous, and not usually materialistic. They might have a darker outlook on life, be into arts and theater, enjoy heady conversations about philosophy, trip over their own feet as they walk, be in their head all the time, have a hard time sticking to one thing, often forget to eat, and suffer the most from anxiety.

The *rLung* humor resides in the energetic, blood, and lymph channel systems. The *rLung* humor flows through the channels of the body. Small electrical currents bring messages of the deposit of body fluids, nutrients, even stress, to various organs and meridians of the body.

The *rLung* humor is responsible for the functions of the heart. The heart is considered the seat of the higher mind in Tibetan Buddhism. It is also responsible for the functions of the lungs, large intestine, nerves, and blood vessels. Because of the intense relationship between the mind of a person and *rLung*, any thoughts we have affect the subtle flow of the current of *rLung* in the body.

THE FIVE TYPES OF *rLUNG*

1. Life-Sustaining Wind

The Life-Sustaining Wind is considered the root of the whole human system. It is the very root of physical incarnation. In Tibetan Medicine, the Life-Sustaining Wind is called *Srog-zhin* (pronounced zog-shin) and is located at the crown of the head, within the brain. It travels down toward the pharynx and esophagus. It is the basis of all life, because this Wind contains the brain, the heart, and the functions of the higher human mind. Without it, life is impossible. It is responsible for:

- Swallowing
- Breathing
- Sneezing
- Stretching
- Yawning
- Clearing the throat
- Concentration of the mind
- The clarity of all the sense organs
- Providing stability of the mind

Anxiety, psychosis, and many forms of mental illness are related to a *srog-zhin* imbalance. Monks who concentrate very hard on extremely esoteric meditations can suffer from *srog-zhin* mental illness.

2. Ascending Wind

The Ascending Wind is located in the general area of the chest, but also circulates throughout the throat, tongue, and nose. It is responsible for:

- Speech
- Complexion
- The shape and tone of the body
- Diligence
- Good concentration
- Memory (poor memory can indicate a problem with *rLung*)
- Self reflection
- The ability to learn

An odd vocal tone in the voice, such as after having a stroke (which is a *rLung* disease), can be related to an imbalance in Ascending Wind.

3. All-Pervading Wind

The All-Pervading Wind is located in the heart region but is also flowing throughout the channels all over the body. It is responsible for:
- Making muscular and joint movement possible
- Enabling mental focus on an object or on study
- Grasping and letting go of an object
- Enabling the physical growth of children
- The continued renewal of skin, hair, cells, etc. in adults
- Graceful, smooth movements of the body
- Coordinated actions of the thinking processes working with the body closely, as in the refined movements of a skilled painter.

4. Descending Wind

The Descending Wind is located in the perineal region, and traverses through the large intestine, urinary bladder, and thighs. It is important in the elimination of all waste from the body, for the discharging of semen, menstruation, and birth contractions.

5. Fire-Accompanying Wind

The Fire-Accompanying Wind is located in the stomach region, and has meridian pathways throughout all the internal organs. It is responsible for:

- Separating nutrients from waste in the metabolism of food.
- Promoting the movement and translation of nutrients into the seven building blocks, or constituents of the body: blood, muscle tissue, fatty tissue, bone, marrow, semen, and ovarian eggs.

The Consciousness Mind

The *rLung* humor is similar to the vital force described in Chinese Medicine as *chi* (*qi*), but there are also differences. Chinese Medicine talks more about this force as energy, whereas Tibetan Medicine describes it as consciousness. Tibetan Medicine describes the consciousness, or mind, as harnessing the *rLung* to create a physical existence so as to have experiences. As a result, anything that pertains to the mind, emotions, or thoughts in Tibetan Medicine can be housed—or located—anywhere in the body.

When We Are Born

You may be more familiar with the Chinese Medicine classification of energy into *yin* and *yang*. In all Asian medical systems, there is a basic splitting of forces that make birth possible. First, there is *rLung* or Wind, which then splits into the first principles of opposites: Bile and Phlegm. Life is not possible without this first differentiation of forces. These two opposing forces then provide tension, structure, and dynamic change—the same qualities of *yin* and *yang*. *Yin* and *yang* can be thought of as dark and light, as night and day, as cold and heat. In Tibetan Medicine these forces are Phlegm and Bile. Phlegm is responsible for cold in the body, and slowing things down, or *yin*. Bile is the humor associated with heat in the body, and speeding things up, or *yang*. If we have a fever, Phlegm is there to pick us up and calm down inflammation that may happen in the throat or mucous membranes. It is thought of as the basic force of cold. If we are cold, Bile warms us up. The actions of both Phlegm and Bile require *rLung*, the primary force, to work.

The mind is the basis of *rLung*. If we can think of life before birth from the Tibetan medical perspective, we would see it as a still pool

If we can think of life before birth from the Tibetan medical perspective, we would see it as a still pool of water, where there is no movement but just the peace of the still water, not even moving slightly. Then the idea of birth takes place. The still pool begins to move.

of water, where there is no movement but just the peace of the still water, not even moving slightly. Then the idea of birth takes place. The still pool begins to move. The consciousness is stirring. It is coming out of its stillness and understanding its connection to the whole. As the pool of water moves, waves appear. This can be thought of as the *rLung* beginning to stir, to make movement. The oneness of mind is differentiating. The idea of birth is taking place.

When this one mind splits off from itself, and the first glimmerings of incarnation are present, this separate, initial mind-self that is formed needs a way to take on the human form. This subtle intelligence can be thought of as wanting to incarnate in human form, but in order to achieve this, it needs a vehicle in the same way that we need transportation to travel a long distance. To further emphasize this point, a rider needs a horse. The *rLung* is the horse, and our mind rides it.

The Interplay of Mind and *rLung*

It all begins with this interplay of the mind with *rLung*, which is why *rLung* is so important in all diseases, but especially those concerning mental health. In Tibetan, *rLung* represents mobility, and *rLung*'s basic function, at incarnation and throughout life, is to carry our mind's "stuff" throughout the channels or meridians of the body. It allows the subtle web of streams of consciousness, in the form of the energy channels, to interlace with muscle, sinew, bones, tendons, and organs.

This subtle energy of mind is basically a movement. Tibetan medical texts debate whether *rLung* and the mind should simply be thought of as one movement versus seeing the mind and *rLung* as distinct and separate movements, which is Dr. Jamling's belief. However, there is agreement among scholars that anything that ascribes to movement in the body is *rLung*, such as carrying nutrients through the blood, respiration, the movement of oxygen through our body, yawning, stretching, walking, or even getting up from a sitting position.

The Will and Getting Up Out of a Chair

Let's say we are sitting still, and we suddenly have the thought of movement. The will and *rLung* combine, and suddenly, the body moves across the room. Are the thought of movement and the actual making of the movement distinct? Because of its moving nature, *rLung* is difficult to see. In fact, if you visualize the wind through the trees, you can have a better idea about *rLung*. It cannot be seen, but we can see its effects: trees bend and leaves move on the branches. This movement of *rLung* is continuous. It begins before we are born and continues throughout our lifetime here. It is this movement that makes possible the launching of the consciousness out of the human state at death and into the next phase of existence. This close union of the mind with *rLung* thus runs along a continuum from the most subtle, reaching all the way back to the very stillness of the Absolute, through life, and even into the intermediate state, after death, even before one chooses one's next life.

POINTS TO PONDER
- The Three Humors are: *rLung* (Wind), *Tipa* (Bile), and *Bad-Gan* (Phlegm).
- The *rLung* carries our mind's "stuff" throughout the body.
- The *rLung* is the platform for streams of consciousness, in the form of the channels, which then interlace with muscles, sinews, bones, tendons, and organs.

The mind is the rider and the horse is *rLung*.
Only the rider has no legs on which to move himself
and the horse has no eyes in which to perceive.
Thus the paralytic mind and the blind horse need each other
in order to function; without *rLung*, mind cannot move,
without mind, *rLung* cannot perceive.
The mind has the power to lead and train the horse,
or misuse and exhaust it. The horse has the ability
to run wild without any sight to where it's going
or stay where the rider does not want.

—Dr. Nyima Tsering

SEVEN

THE FLOW OF rLUNG

The subtle *rLung* energy flows through our body's channels, also called meridians. The energy courses through our body, bringing vitality and force, mobility, and movement to all biological activity. These channels are very similar to the acupuncture meridians of Chinese Medicine. Tibetan medical doctors are taught a very precise anatomy and physiology of the energetic channels through which *rLung* flows. These channels have very specific relationships with vital organs as well as with our emotions. Our minds ride the *rLung*, and our thoughts and emotions are inextricably linked with this vital life force.

Think about how your blood pressure rises when you become angry or frustrated. This is the movement of *rLung*. In fact, *rLung* moves blood. Our minds and emotions are dictating the flow of blood through our body. The *rLung* energy is a very subtle, invisible force, which has physical characteristics as well. We say the liquid by-products of all the organs (such as, blood, mucous, tears, and semen) are all the "sons and daughters" of *rLung*. It's much like the chemistry

opposite:
The Wind Horse,
by Jaye McElroy,
a hand-inked
print on Tibetan
Cloud paper

concept of a solid, liquid, or gas. Water can be solid, like ice, liquid, which we drink, and also steam, a strong and invisible force that can blow the lid off a boiling pot.

A constantly negative chatterbox mind can hound the body and weigh it down. In Tibetan Medicine, if you only treat the body, the mind can still ride roughshod over the physical body, resulting in much illness. Over time, this can result in a decrease in energy and cause imbalances in the organ systems that govern a healthy body as well as the delicate Three Humors of Wind, Bile, and Phlegm. *See Chapter Six for an in-depth explanation of the Three Humors.*

The anatomy charts in Tibetan Medicine bear some resemblance to a Chinese acupuncture meridian chart, and in fact, the underlying principle of a vital force is the same and used in both medical systems. However, in Tibetan Medicine, the *nadis*, or acu-points themselves, are more important than the lines of force (the meridians) between them.

There are three main channels of the body through which *rLung* flows. *(See chart on page 85.)*

Weaving the Basket

The underlying energetic web of *rLung* points can be thought of as a basket. The intertwining, strong, woven reeds are the sinews, bones, and other physical structures. The holes in between emanate out the "great light," or *rLung*, the underlying vitality and force of the *nadis*/acu-points. This metaphor may help in understanding that the *nadis* are more important to Tibetans than the meridian channels themselves. In comparison, Chinese Medicine emphasizes the importance of the meridian systems more than the acu-points. The *nadis* are the focus of traditional Tibetan forms of healing, such as burning herbs on points (moxibustion) or using a Golden Needle (which is actually rarely used in Tibetan Medicine) on the point on the top of the head.

Tibetan Buddhist monks apply the theories of *rLung* energy and the *nadis* in their meditation exercises. In 1981, Dr. Herbert Benson, a physician at Harvard University, studied how Tibetan monks can

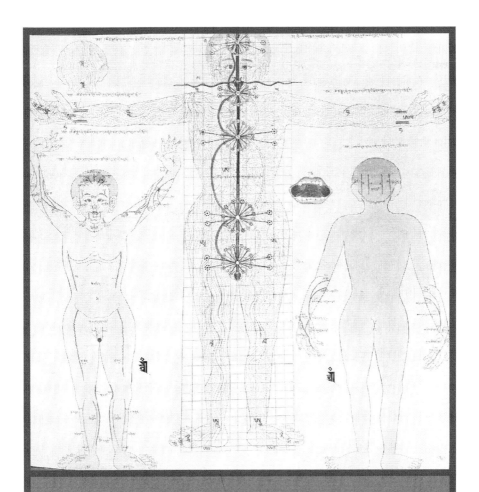

The three main channels of the body through which *rLung* flows are depicted in the central figure of this Tibetan Medical Thangka.[1] You can see that the line on the right is white, the middle is blue, and the left is red. These channels have intersecting points, or *khorla* (pronounced kor-la) that are the main chakras of the body. These main chakras bifurcate out on both sides and connect the *nadis* (or acu-points) in lines of *rLung* throughout the body. Chakras and *nadis* are used in Tibetan Medicine as points for massage, moxibustion (burning herbs on or near the points), and bloodletting (using an acupuncture needle to prick the skin and let a drop of blood come out).

control the movement of *rLung* within their bodies in order to document the understanding in Tibetan Buddhist psychology. Dr. Benson was able to prove that they could alter their body temperatures through the Buddhist practice of the yoga of inner heat or mystic heat, called *gtum-mo*[2] (pronounced tum-mo).

By placing probes in certain locations on the bodies of the *gtum-mo* practicing monks, Dr. Benson was able to calculate, using biomedical measurement tools, that the monks could alter their body temperatures by over 8 degrees Celsius. The *gtum-mo* monks were able to actually dry wet sheets placed on their bodies by using their Tibetan Buddhist meditative exercises. This study demonstrated how Tibetan Buddhist monks are trained in an inner physiology related to *rLung*, whereby they are able to voluntarily generate body heat at will.

The Great Physician

These techniques of Tibetan Buddhist mind/body control stem from Buddhist esoteric scriptures from the 4th century and forward. Buddha, or as the Tibetans refer to him, Shakyamuni Buddha—the Great Physician, is an excellent example of how some of the most brilliant doctors in Tibetan history were also Buddhist monks. The monks take a vow to serve humanity and choose medicine as their field of endeavor. One of the foremost medical doctors was Nagarjuna, the founder of one of the largest schools of Buddhism in the world. In the 4th century, Nagarjuna wrote a brilliant foundational text on herbal medicine entitled, *The One Hundred Prescriptions*. He also wrote The *Precious Collection*, a gathering of medical advice and prescriptions. He, along with other Buddhist monk scholars, helped advance the practice of Tibetan Medicine greatly. Today, these books are still used in Tibetan medical colleges, where earnest and devoted students dedicate four to seven years to become a Tibetan medical doctor.

> *Some of the most brilliant doctors in Tibetan history were also Buddhist monks.*

POINTS TO PONDER
- The *rLung* energy moves blood, and our minds and emotions dictate the flow of blood through our body, even causing our blood pressure to rise when we're angry and upset.
- There are three main channels of the body.
- Where they intersect are what's called *khorla* or chakras.
- The *nadis* are acu-points that are used in massage and moxibustion.

When you think about yourself,
think about all beings being happy.
When you cultivate this bodhicitta,
that goes beyond yourself,
you can never be sick . . .

—*His Holines the Dalai Lama*

EIGHT

MEDITATIONS TO
REDUCE ANXIETY

Meditation in Tibetan Medicine goes back to the time of Shakyamuni Buddha himself (961–881 BC). Sitting under the bodhi tree, Buddha reached enlightenment after struggling in meditation with his mind and his emotions. He experienced frightening projections of his own mind, including demons. Gradually, Buddha was able to calm his mind, and return continually to a centered place within himself. These teachings on meditation were spread throughout Tibet during the reign of King Songtsen Gampo, the founder of the Tibetan Empire, in the 7th century. Buddhist beliefs blended with the local shamanic Bon culture. Buddhist monasteries were built and works on meditation practices were written. Monks often served as doctors, and they blended theories of the mind/body dynamic with their herbal medicine practices, thus creating the unique Tibetan medical system that exists today. The Buddhist tantric meditation practices that outline a subtle, energetic anatomy were incorporated into various texts, such as the *rGyud-bzhi* (gyu-shi), the main Tibetan medical text still currently taught at medical schools.

In Tibetan Medicine, meditation is recommended for calming the emotions and rooting the mind together, thus reintegrating the mind and body into a cohesive whole. We will explore three basic types of meditation in this chapter:

Chanting Mantras meditation—Reciting of prayers and previous names of Buddha.

Mindfulness meditation—Observing one's breath and actions very carefully.

Body scan meditation—Learning to harness the power of the mind to instruct the muscles in the body to relax.

These basic types can get you started down the path of meditation and healing your anxiety. I have compiled these meditation techniques from Dr. Jamling and several Tibetan Buddhist monks I met while working in Dharamsala.

Paving the Way

Before you begin meditation, it's important to get prepared. In the Tibetan Buddhist tradition, it's very important to bring the right attitude of mind to one's meditation practice. Preparatory prayers handed down from the Shakyamuni Buddha and subsequent Buddhist teachers can help generate the proper attitude of mind, making your meditations flow more easily.

Having the right attitude of mind cannot be emphasized enough. Having the right focus and intention before beginning meditation is like putting a saddle on the *rLung* horse so that you can better guide your breath and concentration.

It is imperative that before you begin meditating, you have a pure heart. Preparatory prayers can help purify your heart so your intentions and motivations are true and then can affect your health positively.

Practicing Peace

Find a comfortable straight-backed dining chair, cushion, or spot on the bed where you can sit quietly each day for 5 to 20 minutes. Try to use the same spot every day if possible. You can build up a habit of the mind when you sit in the same spot over time. It's as if the peacefulness of meditation accumulates in the one spot. I started meditating as a teenager when I lived in a small house with precious little space. I created my meditation spot right on my bed with the pillows behind me and my legs crossed. To this day, I still use this spot on my bed, even though my bed has moved many times since those days of discovering meditation. When I drop onto my bed to meditate in the morning or in the evening, I can quickly find my settled state of consciousness, as the habitual mood of the spot and the surroundings immediately uplift me and remind me why I am there.

Light a candle, if possible, or the special *rLung* incense. (*See Resources for information on where to buy this incense.*) This incense calms the mind. I have personally found this special incense to be the most effective for the treatment of anxiety.

 NOTE: *If the rLung incense isn't available to you, you can also try heating lavender and spearmint essential oils together for relaxation.*

Keeping the body comfortable and at a warm temperature is very important. Some people like to have a blanket over their legs; others prefer a shawl to stay warm.

Sit with a relaxed but straight posture. You can sit in a cross-legged or half-lotus position if you're on a bed or on the floor. It's very important to keep your spine comfortably straight so your posture is not rigid. This allows the correct flow of the *rLung* through the channels and will enhance your meditation practice.

Meditation seated position

Cultivating Peace of Mind Before You Begin Your Meditation

Start by dedicating your meditative efforts to the benefit of all human beings, not just yourself. This will help you begin to move out of lower ego states, such as selfishness, suffering, and pain. Simply said, this can help you stop thinking about your own problems, launching your meditation practice to a much more effective level very quickly.

The preparatory Tibetan Buddhism prayers can help you generate compassion and generosity for humanity, the earth, and all its creatures, big and small. I learned the following prayers while sitting with Lama Zopa Rinpoche, Kamtrul Rinpoche, and Shopa Lama in Dharamsala. You can say these prayers aloud or quietly to yourself. These meditations can be used to gently change your mind's dominion over your body. This means they help your mind have more control over your body and its functions.

Choose a prayer that you are comfortable with, or formulate a personal one that might be related to your struggles or your anxiety. If you create your own, include a compassionate prayer for the benefit of other beings, not just yourself. The point of preparatory prayers is to help with motivation and focus before you begin to meditate. This reminds us of our higher nature and path, our destiny to be of service to the wider world.

GENERATING BODHICITTA PRAYER

Bodhicitta (pronounced bodi-chitta) means to make the decision to gain enlightenment, not just for oneself, but for all beings who are suffering. Bringing this attitude to meditation practice can uplift your consciousness and allows your ego to rise above itself, for the sake of all beings. It is the beginning of selfless compassion.

> *Through the virtues I gain through meditating, and giving compassion,*
> *May I achieve enlightenment for the sake of all beings, for the benefit of all beings.*

GENERATING THE FOUR IMMEASURABLES

May everyone be happy
May everyone be free of misery
May no one ever be separated from their happiness
May everyone have equanimity, free from hatred
and attachment

VISUALIZING THE FIELD FOR ACCUMULATING MERIT

In the space before me is the Living Buddha Shakyamuni, and all Buddhas, who were once like me, seeking enlightenment from the Shining One. All Buddhas and Boddhisattvas are with me, like the full moon surrounded by stars.

PRAYER OF THE SEVEN LIMBS

With my body, speech, and mind, I humbly prostrate
And make offerings, both set out and imagined.
I confess my wrong deeds from all time,
And rejoice in the virtues of all.
Please stay until samsara (the dark ages) ceases,
And turn the wheel of dharma for us.
I dedicate all virtues to the enlightenment of all beings.

Chanting Mantras Meditation

Mantra meditation helps the mind to latch onto and focus on a word, idea, or prayer, instead of focusing on chaotic emotions. Most people learn this type of meditation first. It's easy to begin and can be applied in a meditative sitting position. I also chant throughout the day, especially if my mind is restless, or I have a challenging situation. The mantra meditation technique engages the verbal part of our mind and can serve as a distraction away from negativity. As the mind becomes stable, so do the emotions. Throughout the day, you may want to call upon your mantra meditation to help pull your mind and emotions away from anxious thoughts.

THE JEWEL IN THE LOTUS WITHIN OUR HEARTS

In Dharamsala, my neighbor gave me tea every afternoon, and she pleasantly chanted, "*Om Mani Padme Hum!*" over and over again throughout the preparation of it.

According to advice given by His Holiness the Dalai Lama in a lecture in New Jersey,[1] while you recite the mantra *Om Mani Padme Hum*, "you should be thinking on its meaning, for the meaning of the six syllables is great and vast." In the same lecture, he also explained his interpretation of each syllable as follows:

Om "symbolizes the practitioner's impure body, speech, and mind." He also says that it represents "the pure exalted body, speech, and mind of a Buddha."

Mani means jewel and symbolizes "the factors of method: altruistic intention to become enlightened, compassion, and love."

Padme means lotus and wisdom.

Hum indicates indivisibility: "Purity must be achieved by an indivisible unity of method and wisdom."

To simplify, if you dependably practice a path that is both wise and has good methods (meaning if you reliably practice wise meditation), "you can transform your impure body, speech, and mind into the pure exalted body, speech, and mind of a Buddha..."

I asked many locals in Dharamsala what they thought this *Om Mani Padme Hum* prayer meant, and most told me they thought it meant, "the jewel in the lotus," meaning that even though we are imperfect beings, the Buddha nature of enlightenment is inside us, untarnished and ready to be found, like the lotus flower. This is the most common mantra among Tibetans, and they use it all day long, while accomplishing tasks and doing their housework. Dilgo Kyentse Rinpoche, a respected Tibetan Buddhist teacher, tells us:

> The mantra *Om Mani Padme Hum* is easy to say yet quite powerful, because it contains the essence of the entire

teaching. When you say the first syllable *Om*, it is blessed to help you achieve perfection in the practice of **generosity**, *Ma* helps perfect the practice of pure **ethics**, and *Ni* helps achieve perfection in the practice of **tolerance and patience**. *Pad*, the fourth syllable, helps to achieve perfection of **perseverance**, *Me* helps to achieve perfection in the practice of **concentration**, and the final sixth syllable *Hum* helps achieve perfection in the practice of **wisdom**.

So in this way recitation of the mantra helps to achieve perfection in the six practices from generosity to wisdom. The path of these six perfections is the path walked by all the Buddhas of the three times.[2] What could then be more meaningful than to say the mantra and accomplish the six perfections?[3]

Om Mani Padme Hum can carry you through your day when you feel anxious. Try pondering the meaning of the mantra and allow your thoughts to return to their pureness. When in an anxious state of mind, try gripping an object within your reach and saying this mantra quietly as you feel the physical contact of the object grounding your thoughts. One of my clients who experienced severe anxiety while driving would squeeze the steering wheel tightly while saying this mantra aloud. This method gave her concentration, physical grounding, strength, and balance and helped her get on her way and through traffic peacefully.

CALLING ON THE MEDICINE BUDDHA

The Medicine Buddha, as shown on the cover of this book, is an image that you can meditate on to evoke peace of mind. When you call upon the Medicine Buddha, he offers his soothing presence, aiding the sick and helping the dying. The Medicine Buddha, sometimes respectfully referred to as the Blue Buddha, holds in his left hand a bowl made of lapis lazuli with medicine nectar in it. In his right hand, he holds a stem of the Aruna fruit, or Myrobalan, a common herb used in Asian medicine. (*Please visit this book's website, www.HealingAnxietyBook.com* to print out a photo of the Medicine *Buddha*.) To call upon the Medicine Buddha, you recite the Medicine Buddha mantra, which has been recited by Tibetan doctors since the 4th century.

THE MEDICINE BUDDHA MANTRA

The Tibetan pronuciation of the mantra is:
Om Namo Bhagawate Bhaishjaye Guru Vaidurya Prabha Rajaya Tathagataya Arhate Samyaksam Buddhaya Teyatha Om Bekhajye Bekhajye Maha Bekhajye Bekhajye Samudgate Svaha

The translation of this invocation of the Medicine Buddha mantra is:
Om: We begin with Om to pay tribute to the Universe, to that which is without duality.
Namo: Full of trust we yield.
Bhagawate: In intimate relation to the Divine and the complete Universe.
Bhaishjaye: The name of the Medicine Buddha.
Guru: Spiritual Master or "that" which transmutes ignorance into wisdom.
Vaidurya Prabha: Divine deep blue light, like that of lapis lazuli.
Rajaya: Great king.
Tathagataya: Once came or once gone.
Arhate: One who has conquered the cycle of birth and death.
Samyaksam Buddhaya: Perfectly enlightened.
Teyatha: Do it like this.
Om: Again we begin with Om.
Bekhajye Bekhajye: Do away with the pain of illness.
Maha Bekhajye: Do away with the pain of illness (of the darkness of Spiritual Ignorance).
Bekhajye: Do away with the pain of illness.
Samudgate: To the great heights: Like this, go, go, go (my prayer shall go to the highest, the widest, and the deepest).
Svaha: I offer this prayer.

This mantra is longer than some of the others, but with some practice, chanting it comes quite easily. (*Please visit this book's website, www.HealingAnxietyBook.com for a recording of the pronunciation of this mantra.*) You can use it in the morning and evening before beginning your meditation practice. It's traditionally chanted in Tibetan medical clinics whenever moxibustion is used.

Mindfulness Meditation

Mindfulness meditation stems from the times of Shakyamuni Buddha. You start with simple breathing practices in a sitting position. You can also take these basic breathing practices into your daily life, concentrating purely on your breath as you perform any tasks during the day.

ONE THOUGHT AT A TIME

To begin Mindfulness Meditation, follow these steps:

- Sit in a comfortable position with your spine straight, but relaxed.
- Become aware of your body and "check in" with yourself. Feel where your shoulders and each hand are. Feel where your hands rest on your legs and let them relax. Feel the various parts of your body settle into the meditation with acceptance. If parts of you are not relaxed, just let them be in the state they are in. Be aware of where you are, but be gentle with yourself and allow yourself to just be.
- Next concentrate on your breath. Breathe normally. Take a nice, relaxed breath in and then let it out slowly.
- Begin to count your breaths. Breathe in, and then say to yourself as you are doing it, "breathing in." Then as you exhale, say to yourself, "exhaling" and the number one. Count your breaths gently. Feel your body relax, but always return to the breath.

 NOTE: *Our minds can get distracted at this point, but all that needs to happen is to return to the counting. You might get lost. If so, just return to the present moment and start again.*

If you are a beginner, do this for ten minutes and then take a break. Try again later if you like. If you are more experienced, start with twenty minutes twice per day.

Try adding this practice into your daily routine. First, keep in mind that this meditation is about returning to thinking of only one thing at a time. The mind is generally scattered. It thinks it is important that you dwell on an emotional problem, no matter the time of day, or what you are doing. Actually, one can say to the mind, "This is very important, but I will think about it later. Instead, I am going to return to my breath and the activity at hand."

For example, try this exercise while walking up stairs, such as when you're taking in your groceries.

- When you put your foot on the first stair, say, "I am walking on the stair with my right foot, and I am breathing in."
- On the next step, say, "I am now walking on my left foot, and pulling my body forward. I feel the bag in my hands, and I am breathing out."
- Alternatively, you can count the stairs, while breathing, feeling each foot intensely as it hits a new stair.

MEASURING OUR BREATH

This meditation links your mind and body into the counting of time. As Dr. Jamling says, "Your mind is connected to the breath, because of *rLung*. Slow your breath, and you will slow your mind."

> "Your mind is connected to the breath, because of *rLung*. Slow your breath, and you will slow your mind."
> —Dr. (Lady) Dadhon Jamling

In this breathing meditation, you count how long it takes you to inhale, hold your breath, and then count how long it takes you to exhale. It takes your mind away from its worries and gives it something to think about, other than your body or stress.

For this breathing meditation, follow these steps:

- Sit in an upright position, with the spine supple and relaxed.
- Feel the presence of your body accepting (or rejecting) the process of going into quietness. Do not judge your condition,

but be aware of it with compassion. Let your body and mind be as they are. Do not force them to comply. Allow it just to be.

- While inhaling, slowly count how long you breathe in a full breath comfortably. Perhaps to the number seven.
- Hold the breath deep within your belly, pulling the belly button in, for as long as you counted for the inhaling breath. Feel your breath low in your belly rather than up in your chest.
- Exhale, and begin to count how long it takes for your exhale to be comfortable and complete—creating its own number. It will probably be close to the number of your inhale breath.
- Try this for ten minutes. Many people set a gentle timer to help them reach their wanted meditation time.

 NOTE: *If your mind wanders and you lose your place, just return to counting the inhale breath again.*

Gradually, as you do this meditation exercise, you will begin to feel your mind clear. It will take practice but is so worth the effort.

You can start your breathing meditations in your special meditation "spot" at home and then gradually try to bring these practices into your daily life. While counting your breath doing your daily tasks, such as washing dishes, folding clothes, or even taking out the trash, just begin to be aware of your breath and how you actually interact and move through your physical world. The breath work is beneficial because the mind follows the breath. By breathing in while being conscious of the breath, and then breathing out while being conscious of it, you can develop a union of activity of mind and body that brings a wonderful sense of peace.

We can lose countless moments and experiences in life, through the mind running off and being scattered.

The chatterbox mind is distracted by your inner dialogue with the task at hand, bringing you back to the present moment. You become mindful and more aware of what is happening in the actual moment of what you are doing. What a contrast to be eating an apple, for example, while ruminating over a stressful event, being completely unaware of the joy of this wonderful creation called the apple!

We can lose countless moments and experiences in life, through the mind running off and being scattered. When you take charge of your mind, you gently bring the mind back to its proper function: observing acutely the exact task at hand and concentrating purely on doing only that. When you return to the task at hand with these skills, suddenly, you may hear a bird sing. It resonates throughout your body, and your mind is happy. A grateful joy returns, and you become like a child: feeling, breathing, and doing just one thing at a time.

To quiet your chatterbox mind, you can talk internally to yourself about what you are doing. For example, when you eat an apple, you can say:
- "Breathing in, I take a bite of this apple."
- Then say to yourself, "Breathing out, I see the apple in my hands."
- "I am breathing in and biting into this apple."
- "I am breathing out and feel its juices, and how sweet it is in my mouth."
- "Breathing in: another good bite! Wow, it tastes fresh and alive with the energy of the tree it grew on."
- "Breathing out and chewing the skin of the apple, it feels hard on my teeth."

BODY SCAN MEDITATION

Body scan meditation will teach you how to control your muscles, even the brain muscle, which houses the mind. This is a pleasant, relaxing activity for bedtime at the end of the day. It relaxes your body. This meditation exercise involves telling the various parts of the body how to relax.

Start your body scan like this:
- Begin by lying down comfortably.
- Slowly breathe in and breathe out, counting your breaths for approximately five minutes.

- Start at your toes and work your way up the body. First feel your toes. Say to yourself, "My toes are now relaxing." Wiggle your toes and relax. Feel the tension melt away in your toes and their muscles.
- Move your focus to your feet. Feel each foot and its muscles. Feel the tension in the feet. Focus your mind on a foot, and tell it to relax, saying, "I feel my left foot relax." Breathe in and say, "I feel my right foot relax." Then breathe out.
- Next focus on your ankles. Think about the ankles and how much work they do every day. Think and feel acutely, as much as you can, the muscles supporting and surrounding your ankles. Feel them relax. You can also gently rotate them and then actually feel them relax.
- Move your attention to your calves. The calves are very tense on many people. Feel how strong they are. Really put your attention into the back of your legs and get a sense of their dimension, strength, and beauty. Tense them, and then feel them relax. You can even tell your calves, "It's time for bed now . . . it's time to loosen up and relax . . . " They will listen to you.
- Work your way further up your body, relaxing each individual part as you go. You can focus more attention on whatever areas you feel are chronically tight in your body, such as the lower back or neck area. Breathe into the muscles, then breathe out, feeling them release all the pressures of the day. (I almost always concentrate on the lower aspect of my spine. I work my way up the spine, taking in one vertebra at a time. Other challenging parts of the body for me are the nape of my neck and the trapezius muscles from working at a desk, bending over clients, doing bodywork, and standing up making herbal remedies.)
- When you arrive at your head, concentrate on your neck, the jaw, and the muscles of your face. Feel your eyes—feeling the tension just melt out of the eyes is a wonderful thing.

Body scan meditation will teach you how to control your muscles, even the brain muscle, which houses the mind.

- From the eyes, relax the ears and then go inside to the brain. With the brain, say, "Thank you brain! Good job! You're always there for me...now let's relax. It's time for sleep...brain, go to sleep...relax..." The brain listens. Tranquility will enter t he brain.

 NOTE: *The key to the body scan meditation is focus. Whenever your focus wanders, just come back to breathing in and out, observing the body, and continuing the dialogue with the body as you scan.*

Even in the first session, you will get a sense of taking back your power of awareness over bodily rhythms and functions.

Start your body scan meditations lying down and then gradually bring these practices into your daily life. You can see where your body is at any point in the day. As you advance in your exercises, try doing your body scan techniques while doing something uncomfortable, such as giving someone bad news on the phone:

- Start by observing your body to see where exactly you feel tense.
- Breathe in and wiggle your toes in your shoes. Breathe out.
- Feel the phone in your hand. Smell the scents around you as you breathe in and exhale slowly.
- Feel the tension in your shoulders as you are listening on the phone. Feel your neck holding up your head.

By reining in the mind and being in the moment, anxiety dissipates naturally. It gets relegated to back corners of the mind, like hungry wolves—when they aren't fed, they starve and disappear. The slower and more even the breath of the body, the more relaxed the mind becomes. A natural, child-like awareness can come back, returning the simple joys and pleasures to one's life experience.

Body scan awareness meditations are also useful while driving. You can return to center and calmness by becoming acutely aware of your posture and your hands gripping the wheel, while relaxing your shoulders.

Internal talk is an anxious habit the mind loves to play with. An over-stimulated mind filled with stories that go round and round removes one's focus from the actual world and displaces precious human experience, leaving one empty and not truly enjoying the world.

By reining in the mind and being in the moment, anxiety dissipates naturally. It gets relegated to back corners of the mind, like hungry wolves—when they aren't fed, they starve and disappear. The slower and more even the breath of the body, the more relaxed the mind becomes. A natural, child-like awareness can come back, returning the simple joys and pleasures to one's life experience.

POINTS TO PONDER

Before you begin meditation, work on finding a comfortable place to sit that you can return to regularly. Develop a prayerful attitude, bringing pure thoughts to your mind. Choose the type of meditation you wish to do:

- **Mantra meditation**—Reciting of prayers and previous names of Buddhas.
- **Mindfulness meditation**—Observing one's breath and actions very carefully.
- **Body scan meditation**—Learning to harness the power of the mind to instruct the muscles in the body to relax.

Read Chapter 13 for suggestions on how to incorporate these Tibetan Medicine healing techniques into your life.

Actually, when it comes to food and diet, disease prevention is quite logical. You avoid eating anything that puts pressure on the body and in particular the immune system and whatever organs are being challenged. It may sound simplistic, but if one eats a relatively healthy diet with less grease, fatty meats, fried, oily, and heavy foods and avoids a lot of sugary foods and sweets, it is impossible for you to not feel some improvement. When we are talking about the immune system, one needs to protect all the filtering organs: kidneys, lungs, liver along with the spleen. They just cannot do their jobs properly if they are constantly bombarded with the above-mentioned foods. Some of the biggest offenders are ice cream, chocolate, colas, artificial preservatives, colors, flavors, and coffee.

—Dr. Yeshi Dhonden, *Healing from the Source*

NINE

FOOD AS MEDICINE

T ibetan Medicine always takes a gentle approach with diet, recommending different foods based on a person's constitutional type or Humor: *rLung* (Wind), *Tipa* (Bile), or *Bad-Gan* (Phlegm). To understand the best dietary approach to healing anxiety, you must first determine your constitutional type. It is important to re-read *Chapter 6* to determine which of the Three Humors are primary and secondary in your nature.

Dr. Jamling explains:

 The Tibetan medical texts tell us that almost all chronic and internal diseases are due to improper diet and long-term abuse of the digestive system. If one can eliminate foods that do not fit one's constitution, this will help treatment greatly.

Understanding Your Constitutional Diet

 Chapter 6 helped you understand whether you are primarily a *rLung* constitutional type or, more commonly, a mixture of types.

opposite:
The Simple
Tibetan One
Pot Wonder:
Beef Stew

For the *rLung* type of person, nutritious and heavier foods are recommended to help settle the *rLung* energy. Lamb, chicken, butter, molasses, even garlic and ginger, warm soups, and boiled milk with nutmeg—all ground the *rLung* energy. The goal is to make the vital force of the body, the *rLung*, remain where it belongs.

The *Tipa* type of person would be told to stay away from spicy foods, greasy foods, and alcohol and to try to have a diet containing beef, fresh vegetables, yogurt, and milk.

The ideal diet for *Bad-Gan* types helps to manage their delicate digestion by restricting excessive amounts of raw foods. They run cold and need warming up. They need a diet high in protein, with warmly steamed vegetables, and not too many starches. They, unlike their *Tipa* friends, can pour hot sauce liberally on their food.

If you are a mixture of two types, you need to take into consideration the dietary guidelines for both Humors. For example, if you are a combination of *rLung* and *Tipa*, you'd want to avoid spicy foods, while concentrating on feeding your body nutritious meats, warm milk, and further grounding your energy by staying away from coffee, alcohol, or any kind of stimulants.

If you are a combination of *rLung* and *Bad-Gan*, you'd want to increase your intake of nutritious meats, maintain a diet of steamed vegetables (sautéed in oil is also possible, but not raw or cooked in low-quality soy sauce) while avoiding rice, which is both starchy and rough, plus it can overstimulate the *rLung* energy in your body.

The Secret Teachings of the 6 Tastes and the 5 Elements

According to the science of Tibetan healing, food is a very powerful form of medicine. Tibetan Medicine is founded on herbal medicine, and so the science of Tibetan doctors extends to plants and anything that can be digested that comes from the natural world. All food has certain "powers" and "qualities," according to Dr. Jamling. Food can be categorized according to its effects on the Three Humors, as well as its effects on "cold" and "hot" diseases. Dr. Jamling states:

All of the tastes, powers, post-digestive tastes, and qualities of food are very particular. These characteristics come from what we call *byung-ba*. *Byung-ba* means to manifest or bring forth. In English you call this an "Element." Anything that comes into existence has to come via the manifestation of the Five Elements. So each food item has in it certain proportions of the Five Elements. By categorizing the foods in this way, we can use them to heal the diseases of the Three Humors.

The tastes, powers, and qualities of food, drinks, and medicines all have the Earth Element as their base. Then plants are first moistened by Water, then ripened by Fire, moved by Air, and take form as a result of Space. The proportion of the Five Elements in each food determines its taste. There are usually one or two elements that are more pronounced in the formation of the "taste" of a food:

- Earth and Water generate sweetness.
- Fire and Earth create sourness.
- Water and Fire make the salty taste.
- Water and Air make the bitter taste.
- Fire and Air make the spicy-hot taste.
- Earth and Air create the astringent taste.

These are the primary Six Tastes, according to Tibetan Medicine. *See Chapter Four for more information about the interplay of the Five Elements and the Three Humors.*

Once you understand the six primary tastes, you can use the art and science of Tibetan healing anywhere in the world! You can come across a berry in the woods in North America, taste it (making sure it's not poisonous) and because you know that it tastes astringent, you will know how to use it medicinally! This is why Tibetan Medicine has been able to survive and heal people all over the world, developing new herbal and food remedies even in diverse environments.

Tibetan doctors know which Elements are contained in each food, and how the food will affect someone according to their predominant constitution. For example, *Bad-Gan* people strongly express both the Earth and Water Elements. Earth and Water Element foods, which are sweet, would be too cold-producing for them. In fact, those slow *Bad-Gan* people love their food, and dream of cuddling up on the couch with a pint of ice cream—cold and sweet—exactly what will aggravate their constitution!

Think about your own constitution, and what six tastes in foods and herbs would help you remain in balance. How do the six tastes affect the different humors or constitutions? What is good for someone who is primarily *Bad-Gan*? What tastes should they avoid?

Use the table here to guide you. It gives you some guidelines of foods to eat and/or avoid. It also applies to diseases, meaning if you are a *Tipa* constitution with signs of a *rLung* disease, you should learn to avoid foods that aggravate both *Tipa* and *rLung* foods in order to balance both.

TASTE	WHO SHOULD AVOID IT	WHO SHOULD EAT IT
Sweet (Earth + Water)	*Bad-Gan*	*rLung, Tipa*
Sour (Fire+Earth)	*Tipa*	*rLung, Bad-Gan*
Salty (Water+Fire)	*Tipa*	*rLung, Bad-Gan*
Bitter (Space+Air)	*rLung, Bad-Gan*	*Tipa*
Spicy-Hot (Fire+Air)	*Tipa*	*Bad-Gan*
Astringent (Earth+Air)	*rLung, Bad-Gan*	*Tipa*

For more information about food categories, see www.healinganxietybook.com

Often, We Love What is Bad For Our Constitution

When I think about classifying foods into the six tastes and imagining who should eat what, I think of my old boss, Bill. He was a classic *Tipa* constitution. The *Tipa* constitution is primarily the Element of Fire. He was very pioneering, daring, outdoorsy, athletic, and fast. He was ambitious, very successful, and charismatic. We would go out to lunch together, and he always dumped loads of spicy hot sauce on his food, talking a mile a minute. He was hot-headed, too, and would occasionally let loose with language to employees that was emotional, fiery, but quickly passing.

As a *Tipa* type, he shouldn't have been eating hot sauce, ever. In fact, if you look at the chart, you can see that the Hot taste aggravates *Tipa* diseases and *Tipa* people. As a fiery hot *Tipa* man, he should have been eating foods that pacify *Tipa* such as the Bitter and Sweet tastes. The sweet taste is cold, and *Tipa* types need to cool their jets. The bitter flavor helps with their acid reflux, constipation, and detoxification, creating balance in their hot digestive tract, and encouraging good acid/alkaline balance in the stomach and intestines.

One day, Bill and I were out to lunch with our *rLung* friend, Jane. I ordered avocado dip and zucchini salad, which is cooling and astringent (I am primarily a *Bad-Gan* type). Bill reaches for the hot sauce, and in my head I started thinking that I should have grabbed that hot sauce out of his hand, and said, "What are you doing? This is going to give you acid reflux in about an hour. Why don't you take my avocado dip and zucchini salad, as they are cooling, and will soothe your fiery digestive tract. Me? My *Bad-Gan* constitution needs that hot sauce! I barely have any digestive fire to churn up my food and get it moving through my system." Later during dessert, as I was about to dig into strawberries and cream (my favorite), I remembered this type of food is probably not the best choice for me, as my digestion was a bit out of balance and too wet. I slid it over to Jane, our *rLung* friend who naturally runs dry, and said, "Here! My treat." I was happy to see she ate every last bite! The sweet fruits and nutritious dairy, which isn't great for my constitution, could help her to remain centered and grounded, just as it should be with her type of constitution.

Tibetan Food Main Categories

Tibetan Medicine categorizes food into Rough, Light, Soft, or Heavy.

- **Rough** food is anything that is difficult to digest or produces heat and stagnation in the stomach as well as inflammation in the body. It also stirs up the *rLung* energy.
- **Light** food moves very quickly through the system and has less nutritional value.
- **Soft** food is easy to digest and doesn't produce heat in the stomach.
- **Heavy** food is high in protein, moves slowly through the digestive system, and is very nutritious.

Here are some examples:

- **Rough**: brown rice, burnt food, coffee, chocolate, and black tea.
- **Light**: white rice, artificial sweeteners, puffed grains, MSG, low-grade soy sauce, green tea, and steamed or boiled foods.
- **Soft**: Milk and oils.
- **Heavy**: Meat, brown rice, dumplings, sugar.

Understanding Rough Food

Rough food is challenging to understand because it is different for each humor type. Generally speaking, food that is Rough in quality is difficult to digest. However, what is easy to digest for one constitution might be difficult to digest for another, and vice versa. So while we can generalize about food that is difficult for everyone to digest, we have to look at each humor specifically to understand Rough.

To start, foods that are generally difficult to digest for all three humor types include:

- Raw salads and strong spicy greens

- Foods with strong tastes such as bitter melon, beet greens, dandelion leaves, celery, corn, eggplant, horseradish, mushrooms, olives, onions, peas, and peppers.

These foods are also very drying, so they are specifically difficult for the *rLung* type. If you have an imbalance that is too wet, these foods may be helpful to dry things out, as described below in the *Bad-Gan* section.

The following sections describe Rough foods to avoid for each humor type:

FOODS TO AVOID FOR THE *rLUNG* TYPE

Foods that are difficult to digest for the *rLung* constitution include:
- **Roughage**—raw foods and cold salads, strong spicy greens
- **Cold** drinks
- Foods with **strong tastes**, such as bitter melon, beet greens, dandelion leaves, celery, corn, eggplant, horseradish, mushrooms, olives, onions, peas, and peppers
- **Drying** foods, such as crackers, popcorn, white potatoes, beans, and dried fruits

For the sensitive *rLung* Imbalanced stomach, these foods create Wind in a *rLung* constitution person and are very drying.

RECOMMENDATIONS FOR THE *rLUNG* TYPE

- Eat cooked vegetables because warm foods are more easily digested.
- Eat highly nutritious, nourishing, oily, grounding foods that stabilize the lightness of *rLung*, such as cooked grains, cooked vegetables, root vegetables, stewed fruits, nuts, and high quality meats, such as beef.
- Do not eat too many fried foods. They also have a Rough (difficult to digest) quality for everyone, but especially *rLung*.

- Do not take in too many stimulants, such as caffeine, nicotine, and hard alcohol, especially if you have a *rLung* Imbalance.
- Eat foods with a smooth quality such as bananas, hot cereal, pureed soups, rice pudding, and hot spiced milk.

FOODS TO AVOID FOR THE *BAD-GAN* TYPE

Rough foods that are difficult to digest for the *Bad-Gan* constitution include:

- Foods that **create mucous** or **cause edema**, including cake, sweets, wheat, pastas, rice, and any carbohydrate.
- Roughage–raw, fibrous foods

RECOMMENDATIONS FOR THE *BAD-GAN* TYPE

- Eat a small amount of **drying** foods to balance a very wet, mucous body environment. Drying foods soak up the mucous and moisture of the digestive tract. Their drying quality helps to move their sluggish digestion along. The fibrous and spicy qualities hurry up the digestion and move food through the system. These foods include: salads, arugula, and pungent and bitter vegetables, such as artichoke, asparagus, beet greens, carrots, cauliflower, chilies, radishes, turnips, raw onions, and most spices. Most legumes are also drying, such as adzuki beans, black eyed peas, pinto beans, and soy beans.

> *For Bad-Gan, salads are okay in the middle of hot days but not in excess. Most veggies should be steamed or boiled in soups.*
> *–Dr. Leela Whitcomb-Hewitt*

- Eat some **spiced bitter dishes**, such as bitter greens like kale, dandelion greens, collard greens, and bitter melon. However, make sure that these dishes are spiced, for example with curries, because bitter foods are cold in nature and *Bad-Gan* digestive tracts are already cold. You want to avoid creating too cool an environment in the digestive tract.

- Eat some **astringent** foods because they wick out the moisture from the digestive tract, like squeezing out a sponge. These include: apples, cranberries, pomegranates, artichokes, broccoli, cauliflower, lettuce, rye, rice, and crackers in small amounts.

FOODS TO AVOID FOR THE *TIPA* TYPE

Rough foods that are difficult to digest for the *Tipa* constitution include:

- **Spicy** hot foods—you want to favor cooling foods over hot and spicy foods.
- **Alcohol**
- **Fried** foods—the oily, hot nature of the fried foods wreaks havoc on the *Tipa* digestive tract by producing too many strong acids to digest the very dense fried food.

RECOMMENDATIONS FOR THE *TIPA* TYPE

- Eat **cooling** vegetables that are sweet and bitter in flavor, such as artichoke, asparagus, beets, broccoli, brussels sprouts, cabbage, carrots, cauliflower, celery, cilantro, cucumber, fennel, green beans, leafy greens, and leeks. These foods help cool the *Tipa* type, which runs hot.
- **Raw** fruits and vegetables—the *Tipa* constitution has an incredible amount of strong digestive fire, so they can eat almost anything that is raw. However, if you are suffering from an *rLung* Imbalance, you would want to lightly sauté or steam these vegetables, so that you get the benefit of the cooling properties, but without injuring the *rLung*.
- Avoid **drying** foods with a pungent quality because they heat up the *Tipa* system too much. These include: beet greens, burdock root, fresh corn, daikon radish, eggplant, garlic, spicy foods, horseradish, kohlrabi, mustard greens, turnip greens, watercress, radishes, and spinach.

NOTE: *Fried foods are difficult to digest for everyone, but especially* rLung *and* Tipa *people. For the Bad-Gan type, sweet chocolate cake is very difficult to digest because it takes a toll on their cold stomachs, as sugar is very cold.*

It's All About Balance

Healing Anxiety is mostly about balancing the *rLung* humor. However, any of the three humors can get out of balance. In the next section, we will go in detail over the foods that help balance and pacify *rLung*. But for those who have a *Tipa* or *Bad-Gan* constitution, it's important to know what an imbalance of your humor would look like.

With a *Tipa* Imbalance, the person becomes extremely angry for no reason, and can suffer from acid reflux, acne, and insomnia. They can wake up to an incredibly sensitive and growling stomach that needs food right away. For *Tipa* Imbalance we need to nourish and cool the digestive tract to pacify and mollify the hot nature of *Tipa*. To do so, one would favor foods of a cooling nature, such as cucumbers, white rice, yellow squash, zucchini, or any water-containing foods that help soothe the digestive tract. The sweet flavor and dairy also create moisture and mucous that the *Tipa* individual may be lacking. They can use soothing coconut oil every morning, massaging their joints, stomach, and limbs followed by a shower, but just lightly washing off the oil, allowing it to sink in and cool the muscular tissue.

For Tipa *Imbalance we need to cool the digestive tract to pacify and mollify the hot nature of* Tipa.

With a *Bad-Gan* Imbalance, we think about someone who is overweight, and yet continues to eat foods that aggravate *Bad-Gan*. *Bad-Gan* people run cold. They put on weight very easily. So they need to stay away from sugars and carbohydrates because these foods increase cold and also are mucous and moisture forming, which wreaks havoc on the *Bad-Gan* digestive tract. With a *Bad-Gan* Imbalance, we want to warm them up and get rid of the edema. We would put them on a strict diet with no sugar or carbohydrates and instead would have them eat small frequent meals of lightly cooked vegetables, but also some small salads. Raw salads can be too cold, and hard to digest, but the roughage is good to get that slow digestive tract going. So with a cold, raw, small salad, we would add some spices—hot sauce or a curry dressing—to aid in the digestion of these raw foods. *Bad-Gan* people have a cold digestive tract that always needs warming up. They should throw hot sauce on everything, favor curries, and drink only warm or hot drinks. All mucous-producing foods should be lessened such as dairy, cheese, sugars, and all those nice pies and cakes that *Bad-Gan* individuals love to make.

Bad-Gan people have a cold digestive tract that always needs warming up.

Foods that Pacify *rLung* and Help Reduce Anxiety

Next, let's take a look at foods that will help pacify *rLung*, for someone who is currently experiencing anxiety. This list is generalized for all *rLung* Imbalance. For each type of person, you can add or modify according to the six tastes that match the person's constitution. In general, *rLung* people and those suffering from *rLung* Imbalance, should eat foods that are warming and nutritious. They should avoid raw foods and also foods that are difficult to digest or are over-stimulating. As Dr. Jamling states:

> To balance *rLung*, there are particular foods that act as medicine, such as nettles, asofoetida dissolved in warm milk, and long pepper[1] mixed in with cooked whole grains.

BUILDING YOUR DIET AROUND THESE FOODS

The following is a table of foods that help pacify *rLung*, organized by food categories. Use the lists to identify and eliminate foods that do not fit your constitution. Make a list of foods you need to eliminate, and refer back to the list until you are comfortable with your choices. Then focus on what you CAN eat and enjoy!

FOODS THAT HELP PACIFY rLUNG/WIND

FRUITS
Apple (cooked)
Apricots
Bananas
Cherries
Cobra lily
Dates
Fig (cooked)
Grapes
Lemon
Mangoes
Oranges
Papayas
Peaches
Pear (cooked)
Plantain (cooked)
Plum
Pomegranate

GRAINS
Amaranth grain
Barley
Beer (warm)
Millet
Oats
Rice (white)
Wheat

VEGETABLES
Adzuki beans
Avocados
Beans (broad)
Beans (french)
Beets (cooked)
Cabbage
Carrot
Cauliflower
Chillies
Corn
Kale
Leeks
Long peppers
Mallow
Mushroom
Mustard leaves
Nettles
Okra
Onion
Pumpkin
Radish (cooked)
Scallions
Soy milk
Spinach
Squash
Turnips

MEATS
Broths (all meat broths)
Buffalo
Chicken
Lamb
Mutton
Yak

SPICES
Angelica root
Asofoetida
Basil (Holy Tulsi)
Cardamom
Cinnamon
Cloves
Cumin
Garlic
Mint
Nutmeg
Parsley
Saffron
Solomon's seal

NUTS/SEEDS
Almonds
Caraway seeds
Cashews
Coconut
Flax seeds
Sesame seeds
  (black and white)
Sunflower seeds
Walnuts

FATS/OTHER
Apple cider vinegar
Barley wine
Bone marrow
Butter
Buttermilk
Ghee
Honey
Milk (boiled)
Molasses
Mustard oil
Seed oils
Sour cream
Sugar
Yogurt

POINTS TO PONDER

- Your constitution is either one of the Three Humors or a combination of two Humors. It is possible, though rare, to be a combination of all Three Humors.
- Based on your constitution, you should eat or avoid certain tastes and certain types of food on a regular basis to stay in balance or get you back into balance.
- To reduce anxiety, you can eat foods from the table that pacify rLung, while being careful to also cross-reference with any restrictions of the other Humors that might make up your constitution.
- *Read Chapter 13 for suggestions on how to begin a 13 Day Retreat for balancing the Three Humors.*

RECIPES TO LIVE BY: CALMING AND BALANCING FOODS

Tibetan Medicine recipes are commonly used to pacify *rLung* and balance all Three Humors in the body.

MILLET PORRIDGE

Eat and enjoy one small bowl each morning throughout the week.

INGREDIENTS

1 cup millet

2 ¼ cups of water

1 tsp butter

1 pinch of salt

Cinnamon (to taste)

Dark grade B maple syrup (to taste)

DIRECTIONS

Preparation time approximately 30 minutes

1. Take the millet and sift it for stones. Rinse and strain millet.

2. Add the millet and water into a saucepan.

3. Add the butter.

4. Add a pinch of salt.

5. Bring to a boil, cover pot and simmer for 20–25 minutes, until the water has boiled down and away.

NOTE: *You can add cinnamon and dark grade B maple syrup to taste. Serve with a small amount of butter on top if needed for taste.*

KITCHARI IN THE KITCHEN

Kitchari (pronounced kitch-r-ee) translates to mean "mixure." When eaten over several days, this nourishing dish detoxifies the body and mind. The fennel herb in this recipe is good for lubricating the digestive tract, and it pacifies *rLung*/Wind.

INGREDIENTS

1 cup whole mung beans

1/2 cup brown or white basmati rice

3 cups water

3 tbsp ghee

1 inch piece of fresh ginger root, peeled and chopped finely

1 tsp fennel seeds, crushed

1 tsp cumin seeds, crushed

3 cinnamon sticks

1/2 tsp turmeric powder

Fresh or sautéed vegetables (optional)

Cooked chicken or beef (optional)

DIRECTIONS

Cooking time approximately 1 hour

1. Boil the water in a medium size pot.

2. Thoroughly wash the mung beans and the rice.

3. Combine the mung beans and the rice.

4. Add them rapidly to 3 cups of boiling water.

5. Add 3 tbsp of ghee.

6. Bring to a boil again, cover, turn the heat down to low, and simmer for 45 minutes.

7. Sauté on medium heat the ginger, fennel seeds, cumin seeds, cinnamon stick, and turmeric in butter or ghee.

8. Add the sautéed seed mixture to the pot when the water is no longer covering the beans and rice but the mixture is not yet fully cooked.

9. At this point you may add any fresh or lightly steamed vegetables to the pot. You can also add cooked chicken or beef if you desire.

10. Simmer for another 10 minutes, or until the water is completely absorbed and the mung beans are firm to the touch (al dente).

THE TIBETAN ONE POT WONDER: BEEF STEW

Meat is a big component in most Tibetan diets, and this recipe is all about the beef! This basic stew pacifies *rLung* and nourishes all three humors. It can be modified by adding nettles, an herb that calms *rLung* and eases toxicity in the digestive tract. This toxicity is often a side effect of *rLung* Imbalance. Other vegetables from the list of beneficial vegetables for *rLung* Imbalance, can also be added.

INGREDIENTS

2 lbs of stewing beef (beef that is still
    attached to the bone, such as a rib eye,
    or beef rib, is usually suggested)

3 tbsp butter

1 onion, roughly chopped

1 tbsp ginger, peeled and sliced

5 carrots, chopped

1 tbsp tomato paste

2 cups fresh nettles or 1 cup dried nettles

1 tsp Powdered nutmeg

DIRECTIONS

Cooking time approximately 1 hour

1. In a large pan (that can fit 10 cups of water),

   brown the beef in the 2 tbsp butter, until all sides

   are crisped and browned.

2. Add the onion, and cook until the onion

   appears translucent.

3. Stir the ginger into the mixture. Add the chopped carrots,

   the nettles, and the remaining 1 tbsp of butter.

4. Brown in the pan on low heat for 10 minutes.

5. Add the 10 cups of water, tomato paste, and nutmeg.

6. Bring to a boil, and then set the pan to simmer

   for 45 minutes.

7. Enjoy and feel nourished and balanced.

NOTE: *If you are using dried nettles, you can skim them off the top while the dish is simmering.*

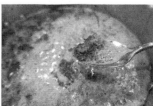

Originally Kunye [Tibetan Massage] is thought to have developed from the practice of early tantric yogis who used various methods, such as oil massage and acupressure points on themselves to keep the *rLung* force flowing properly, and also get rid of stagnation of any sort. Stagnation affects the mind. It can bring difficulty controlling the mind and subtle channels when meditating. If one is healthy and free of blocks and stagnant energy; naturally the flow of one's life-force increases, the mind is clearer, and emotions are more stable.

—*Dr. (Lady) Dadhon Jamling*

TEN

HEALING *rLUNG* WITH TIBETAN MASSAGE

Tibetan therapeutic massage is one of the oldest forms of massage. Massage is one of the most effective ways to pacify *rLung* and relieve anxiety. It is one of the external therapies found in the *rGyud-Zhi* (Four Tantras) for treatment of *rLung* Imbalance and related stress disorders. According to the *rGyud-Zhi*, *rLung* is the sole cause of all disorders.

You can use these massage techniques to treat *rLung* Imbalances, or you can use this massage to prevent *rLung* Imbalance from occurring or re-occurring. The massage treatment described in this chapter has two components:

- A warm oil massage.
- The creation and use of compresses that you can use to enhance the treatment by pressing them on *rLung* points.

Preparing for the Massage

Find a quiet spot where the recipient can lie down, feel safe, warm, and relaxed. Place a sheet down on the area so that any oil that may

opposite:
Tibetan Massage compresses

spill does not stain what is underneath. Light some *rLung* relaxation incense for a few moments. (*See Resources for information on where to purchase the incense.*)

While your patient is relaxing with the incense on the massage table or bed, you'll need five minutes prep time to mix and warm the massage oil according to the recipe below. You can also buy the massage oil and compresses. (*See Resources for information on where to purchase massage oil and compresses.*)

Making the Massage Oil

In a saucepan, mix together the following ingredients:
- 2 tsp ground fennel (or star anise)
- 2 tsp caraway seeds
- 2 tsp ground nutmeg
- 1 cup sesame oil, enough to cover the mixture in the pan

Warm the mixture in the pan, stirring occasionally for 5 minutes. Do not burn the oil.

After the massage oil is finished, you will be creating small warm compresses to put on the *rLung* points.

Making the Compresses

1. Cut six four-inch by four-inch squares from an old sheet or thin towel.
2. Place one square down on a plate or tray.
3. Place one heaping tablespoon of the warmed mixture (with mostly the herbs in it) into the small square of fabric.
4. Wrap it up, twisting it on the top, so that the top serves as a handle to hold when you press the *rLung* points on the body.
5. You can also wrap a rubber band around the top to hold the compress in place if you would like.
6. Continue making the rest of the compresses (six in total).

The Massage

Have the person lie face down on the sheet. Gently wave the special incense near the person's face so the person can breathe it in and begin to relax before the massage begins. Place a bowl of warm oil beside you and a tray or plate of the six warm compresses that you've made with the herbs from the oil mixture.

With the person lying face down, start by rubbing some of the oil on your hands and then gently massage the person's neck, back, legs, and feet. Make sure that your strokes are mostly downward movements, from the back toward the sacrum, and from the legs toward the feet.

Begin to apply one of the compresses lightly with clockwise circular motions on the points in the order they are listed in the diagram on the next page. Go through the points three times. If your wrap gets dried out, refill it by placing it in the oil, which will strengthen the power of the herbs in the compress. Use a new compress as needed. The diagrams on the following pages will show you where to press and massage the compresses more deeply.

If the points are sensitive, take some additional time on them until the area relaxes.

Compress on the 6th Thoracic Vertebra point

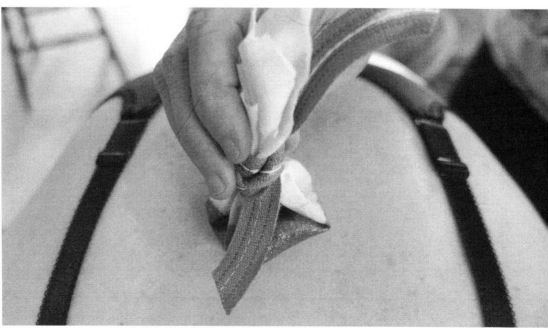

DIAGRAM OF rLUNG POINTS

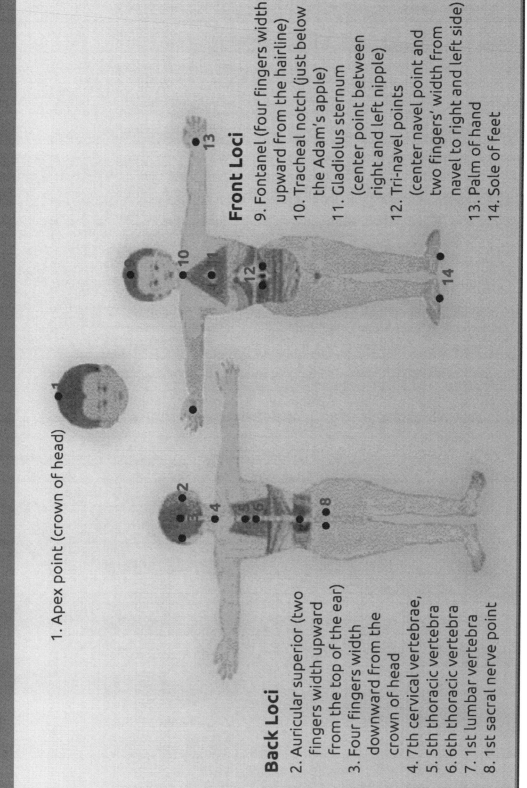

1. Apex point (crown of head)

Back Loci

2. Auricular superior (two fingers width upward from the top of the ear)
3. Four fingers width downward from the crown of head
4. 7th cervical vertebrae,
5. 5th thoracic vertebra
6. 6th thoracic vertebra
7. 1st lumbar vertebra
8. 1st sacral nerve point

Front Loci

9. Fontanel (four fingers width upward from the hairline)
10. Tracheal notch (just below the Adam's apple)
11. Gladiolus sternum (center point between right and left nipple)
12. Tri-navel points (center navel point and two fingers' width from navel to right and left side)
13. Palm of hand
14. Sole of Feet

Apex Point

Located at the top of the head

Apex Point
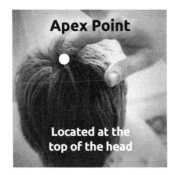
Located at the top of the head

Auricular Superior Point

2 fingers width above the tip of the ear

1) **The Apex point:** This point is located on the top of the head. It is called Governing Vessel (GV) 20 in Chinese Medicine.
For a description of how to locate this point, see the Golden Needle Moxibustion section of Chapter 12.

2) **Auricular Superior point:** Two fingers width upward from the tip of the ear on the side of the head. This point is called Gall Bladder (GB) 8 in Chinese Medicine.

Back of the Head Point
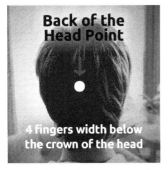
4 fingers width below the crown of the head

7th Cervical Vertebra Point
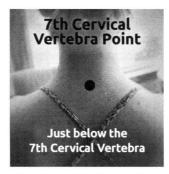
Just below the 7th Cervical Vertebra

5th Thoracic Vertebra Point
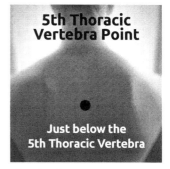
Just below the 5th Thoracic Vertebra

3) **Back of the Head point:** Four fingers width down from the crown of the head. This is called GV 18 in Chinese Medicine.

4) **7th Cervical Vertebra point:** This is located in the vertebral space just below the 7th Cervical vertebra. It is called GV 14 in Chinese Medicine.

5) **5th Thoracic Vertebra point:** This is located in the vertebral space just below the 5th Thoracic vertebra. It is called GV 11 in Chinese Medicine.

6th Thoracic Vertebra Point
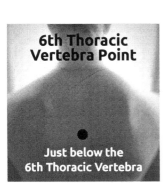
Just below the 6th Thoracic Vertebra

1st Lumbar Vertebra Point
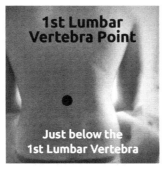
Just below the 1st Lumbar Vertebra

1st Sacral Nerve Point
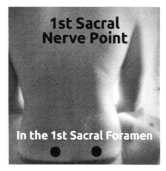
In the 1st Sacral Foramen

6) **6th Thoracic Vertebra point:** This is located in the vertebral space just below the 6th Thoracic vertebra. It is called GV 10 in Chinese Medicine.

7) **1st Lumbar Vertebra point:** This is located in the vertebral space just below the 1st Lumbar vertebra. It is called GV 5 in Chinese Medicine.

8) **1st Sacral Nerve point:** This is located in the first sacral foramen on the sacrum. It is called Bladder 27 in Chinese Medicine.

Once you have done all the points on the top of the head and back, ask the person to turn over slowly and relax on their back. Keep them warm by covering them up with a sheet or towel. Pull back the sheet as needed to reach and gently massage each point. Before you begin applying the compresses, massage the person's shoulders and legs with oil, being respectful and staying within the comfort zone of your patient.

THE POINTS ON THE FRONT

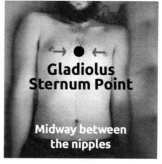

9) The Fontanel point: This point is located four fingers width up from the hairline on the forehead on the midline. It is one body inch above GV 22 in Chinese Medicine.

10) The Tracheal Notch point: This point is located in the depression at the base of the throat called the suprasternal notch. It is called Conception Vessel (CV) 20 in Chinese Medicine.

11) The Gladiolus Sternum point: This point is located midway between the nipples on the sternum. It is called CV 17 in Chinese Medicine.

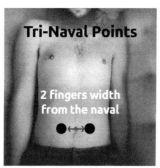

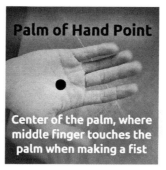

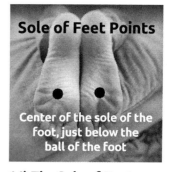

12) The Tri-Navel points: This point is located two fingers width from the navel to the outside (lateral to the navel) on both the left and right sides. It is called Stomach 25 in Chinese Medicine.

13) The Palm of Hand points: This point is located in the center of the palm, where the middle finger touches when you make a fist. It is called Pericardium 8 in Chinese Medicine.

14) The Sole of Feet points: This point is located in the center of the soles of the feet, just below the ball of the foot. It is called Kidney 1 in Chinese Medicine.

When you are using the herbal compresses, remember to spend more time on points that feel tight and need more relaxing.

At the end of the massage, it's important that the person doesn't get cold. Wipe off any excess oil on the body. Allow them to gently get up in their own time. Leave them for a moment to be alone with the incense or soft music to connect back to real time again.

Instruct them that after the massage, a short warm shower or bath is suggested, followed by soup or a warm tea made with nettles and peppermint or chamomile.

POINTS TO PONDER

- Tibetan Massage can be used to treat *rLung* Imbalances or to keep *rLung* Imbalances from re-occuring.
- Use compresses filled with warm oil on specific points.

THE POINTS ARE:

- GV 20
- Gall Bladder (GB) 8
- Governing Vessel (GV) 18
- GV14
- GV 11
- GV 10
- GV 5

- Bladder 27
- GV 22
- Conception Vessel (CV) 20
- CV 17
- Stomach 25
- Pericardium 8
- Kidney 1

The Five Tibetan Rites stimulate the chakras and their corresponding nerve plexuses and glands. By balancing the psychic energies of the body-mind, they promote a strong immune defense system, maintaining a keenly developed nerve transmission, and establish a balanced hormonal climate. They tone and stretch major muscle groups, creating a strong, flexible physique.

—Christopher Kilham
Inner Power: Secrets from Tibet and the Orient

ELEVEN

TIBETAN HEALING EXERCISES

These Tibetan Medicine exercises come from ancient Buddhist scriptures on the stabilization of the mind and body. They equalize the flow of *rLung* in the subtle channels of the body.

The exercises in this chapter are grouped into two sections:

- **Three Tibetan Healing Exercises**
- **Five Tibetan Rites**

In our own culture, doctors recommend cardiovascular exercise for anxiety, and consider it "medicine" for the body. What's important about these Tibetan exercises is that they open up blocked areas of the body and ensure the smooth flow of *rLung*.

The ancient theory behind all these exercises is that they stimulate small energetic centers in your body, called the *nadis*, as discussed in *Chapter 7: The Flow of rLung*. These *nadis* centers are also connected to your glands, nerves, and organs. These energetic points become opened, soothed, and cleansed during these healing exercises.

Read over these exercises, and please consider your age, weight, and how much you are currently exercising in general. Start off very

opposite:
Tibetan
Rite #4

131

slowly. Even though the Tibetan medical texts ask that you do a certain number of exercises, proceed at your own pace. Remember you want to perform each movement the same number of times, when grouping the movements together in one exercise set.

The Three Most Profound and Powerful Tibetan Healing Exercises

When I was studying at Oxford University, back from fieldwork for a few months and writing up my research, I met a scholar who had traveled all over Tibet and was well respected by many extremely advanced yogis of both Tibetan and Indian religious traditions. He spent some time in my small town of McLeod Ganj, and it was enjoyable to have a companion familiar with my strange life in another culture.

It turns out he was given secret oral teachings from Shopa Lama, whom I also knew very well. Shopa Lama used to run out of his small shack whenever I passed by. He wanted me to come in and have some butter tea. I always did! Sometimes he would start chanting and throwing mustard seeds at me, or he would make me sit in meditation with him. I had no idea what he was doing most of the time. He said I would understand many years later. We had a deep love and affection for each other.

At Oxford, my friend taught these healing exercises to a small group of us every Tuesday night. The three exercises, practiced extremely slowly—at a glacial pace—took at least two hours to complete! When we finished doing the exercises, we would come out of the room to the outside sky, and begin singing with such ecstasy. The change in consciousness for us all was extremely profound. One evening, my friend and I came out of the building walking extremely slowly. We felt like we were communicating telepathically, when we turned glacially slowly toward each other and held hands. For many minutes, we looked deeply at one another, exclaiming in whispers that each of us was so divine, so pure, so perfect, and the very expression of God.

The extremely slow movements open up the *nadis*, and cause the vital force, the *rLung*, to flow freely. The extremely slow pace of movement is what opens the channels. We are returning our consciousness, our minds, to the pace of the universe, and coming into tune with the essence of our being. These exercises are phenomenal.

While these and many other exercises and practices were considered sacred and secret for generations, the more esoteric teachings of Tibetan Buddhism are now being released in order to preserve them for posterity. To understand how and why they are being revealed at this time in history, I recommend watching the movie, *The Yogis of Tibet.*[1]

The three anxiety-relieving Tibetan healing exercises are well-known and commonly practiced in Dharamsala. However they are not very well known in the West. These exercises are recommended for healing anxiety but also can be used for prevention of any mental illness. They are a very effective way of treating panic, anxiety, insomnia, and depression, making the person feel more grounded, with a relaxed wakefulness. The exercises aid in grounding the *rLung* energy properly throughout the body. They concentrate on smoothing the passages, or channels, between the top, middle, and lower parts of the body, and result in the smooth flow of *rLung* in the right, middle, and left channels. It's best to perform these exercises at the times when the *rLung* is strong: early morning and dusk.

These exercises are meant to be done slowly and steadily. Incremental, small movements make up one large gesture. It is vitally important to do these movements slowly. These exercises are not like modern day workouts. If you perform a full set of all of these, it would take almost two hours. This may seem difficult to do at first, but with persistence, by the end of the set, it is easily achieved. The breathing and the slowness of the movements slow down the thought processes, thus bringing a union of body and mind, resulting in extreme tranquility. By accomplishing the slow movements, the mind is slowed down, and it settles into a synchronous rhythm with the body.

If you do these exercises once per day, for three days in a row, you'll notice that you have more energy and yet at the same time are relaxed.

THE HEAD ROLL

1.

5.

2.

6.

3.

7.

4.

8.

Time: Approximately 45 minutes

The head roll exercise should be done in the standing position. It should be performed slowly, first clockwise to your right, then counter-clockwise to your left, three times. It's important to complete three head rolls to the right followed by three head rolls to the left. Remember, slow and fluid movement.

• Begin by standing with your legs shoulder-width apart, eyes looking straight ahead.

• Place your hands down beside you, relaxed with your arms feeling weightless. With an awareness of your middle finger on each hand, lightly touch the outer sides of your thighs.

• Take a deep breath in, hold for three seconds, and exhale slowly and deeply. Feel the breath as it comes out.

• Breathe in again, gently pulling in the navel area, and exhale, breathing out slow and steady.

• Start the head roll by bending your head forward, your chin down towards your chest. Breathe in. Exhale and begin to roll your head to the right, very slowly, inch by inch. As you are rolling, inhale and exhale slowly, keep your breathing slow, relaxed, and steady. Allow your head to feel heavy as it moves. Keep rolling, at a glacial pace. It should take at least three to four minutes to reach the halfway point (head tilted back). Moving very slowly with the completion of, for example, one rotation of the head clockwise, takes about seven minutes!

NOTE: At times during this head roll, you may come to a painful area or body part. Breathe into that area. Relax into that area. Take your time, and allow the roll to pause for a moment . . . Breathe, and then move on as the weight of the head continues the movement. Going into the painful area with gentle breath will help open the closed nadis, *which is the source of the pain. The head roll should be easier next time around.*

• When your rotation reaches the back of the head, your chin should be turned up toward the sky, and you feel the stretch of the front of your neck along the front of your throat.

• Continue rolling your head in the same direction until your chin is resting back on your chest.

• Exhale and raise your head back to the starting position.

NOTE: This completes one Head Roll Exercise to the right or clockwise.

• Repeat the above steps going in the same direction (to the right) two more times (for a total of three times to the right).

• After completing three clockwise head rolls, begin your head rolls to the left (counter-clockwise movement).

• Continue until you've done three head rolls to the left.

THE BACK ROLL

1.

2.

3.

4.

5.

6.

7.

8.

9.

10.

Time: Approximately 20 minutes

The back roll is important for opening the *rLung* points on the lower back. It also massages the sides of the legs, and brings energy flow out of your perineal area to the torso, flowing both up and down your back. The art of rolling is to simply relax into the exact position you're in, while maintaining slow but steady breaths. On exhale, roll just 1/8th of an inch, and again breathing, relaxing into the position, then breathing out, and moving 1/8th of an inch. The practice is one of relaxing into each moment, where you can feel the muscles in the lower back relax, as you are pressing onto them. It's like giving yourself a lower back massage, using the pressure of your own body.

• Begin by lying flat on your back, with a mat, towel, or pad underneath you for gentle support if needed.

• Stretch your legs out wide in front of you, palms facing up on the floor or mat. Allow your head to rest on the floor, your eyes half open, looking up and feeling relaxed.

• Breathe in, and pull the navel back gently. Exhale your breath, deeply, feeling the breath leaving your abdomen.

• Bring your knees up to your chest. Hold your knees with your palms gripping the knees. Keep your head completely on the floor for support.

• Take a deep breath in and hold it in just long enough to have the lungs linger and bring the fresh air to the lower lobes of the lungs, then breathe out.

• As you begin to exhale, still holding your knees, start to move your body to the right, very slowly, with tiny millimeter movements toward the floor on your right side. Your feet should be completely relaxed, your toes relaxed, your legs relaxed. Your hands should only be holding your knees in lightly. Keep your breathing slow and steady.

• Keep slowly rolling until your right leg and right arm touch the floor.

• Relax into this position. Breathe in, pull the navel back, exhale slowly, feel the breath leaving the body, and while still holding onto your knees in a relaxed way, begin to move back to the starting position slowly and steadily.

• Once back to center starting position, breathe in, staying relaxed.

• Continue the movement to the left side, turning and slowly moving down, holding the knees lightly until your left leg and hand lightly touch the floor. This completes two rotation exercises: one to the right side and one to the left side.

• Repeat this exercise two more times, for a total of six movements.

• After the six movements are completed, allow your legs to gently drop to the left side and continue to relax, breathing slow and steady.

• Stretch your legs out while turning onto your back. Relax your legs, and place your palms down on the floor. Take your time getting up, and continue the rhythmic slow breaths.

• Slowly rise up to a standing position and breathe in, pulling in the navel area, then exhale and feel the breath leaving your body.

• Smile.

SWAYING TREE IN THE WIND

1.

2.

3.

4.

5.

6.

7.

8.

9.

10.

11.

12.

Time: Approximately 45 minutes

This simple TIbetan Healing Exercise helps the central channel. It opens your heart, stretches your core, and loosens the *nadis* on each side of your body, along the sides of the ribcage, and the central channel, or Life Channel, containing your innermost heart and mind. It smooths the flow of your consciousness through the Central Channel and also loosens muscle and stretches the fascia, releasing long-held toxins and fluids. While doing this exercise, keep your eyes open gently, while breathing rhythmically, and really feel the stretch as you sway in the wind. Remember to do this exercise as slowly as possible.

• Stand with your legs shoulder-width apart.

• Place your hands down at your sides and relax your arms so they feel weightless.

• With an awareness of your middle finger on each hand lightly touching the outer sides of your thighs, take a deep breath in.

• As you exhale, turn your palms outward and allow your arms to rise very slowly. As your arms rise, feel them stretch. Keep breathing in and out, moving ever so slowly with each breath.

• Let your arms rise above your shoulders until they are above your head, straight up if possible for you. The palms of your hands should be facing each other.

• Breathe in, pulling in at the navel area.

• As you exhale the breath, slowly reach up and stretch your fingertips up to the sky.

• Breathe in and imagine yourself to be a tall and mighty tree. Moving ever so slightly, and very slowly, bend to the right with your arms outstretched. The tree is moving ever so slightly.

• Exhale and bend a bit more to the right.

• Pausing in this spot, breathe in and pull in the navel area, becoming aware of your body in this position. Then slowly move toward the center, inching the swaying "branches" of the tree (your arms) back to your starting position.

• As you exhale, make your tree arms move backwards, arching your back ever so slightly backward. Do not force your body back, but gently find the spot that is your arched tree, with your arms having a stretch, but do not strain yourself. You shouldn't be arched back more than two inches. Breathe in slowly, breathe out slowly, and move very slowly, feeling the stretch in your back.

• Return slowly to the starting position with your arms still above your head. This completes the exercise for the right side.

• Repeat for the left side. This is one complete cycle of this exercise. You will ideally complete nine cycles of left/right movements.

SPINNING LIKE A TOP

1.

2.

3.

4.

1.

2.

3.

4.

5.

THE FIVE TIBETAN RITES

Tibetan yogis today still practice the ancient Five Tibetan rites to keep the *rLung* energy flowing smoothly through the body for youthful rejuvenation. Christopher Kilham[1] first wrote about these rites in 1988. These exercises are discussed in detail with added historical background in Peter Kelder's book, *The Eye of Revelation*.[2]

Tibetan Rite #1 – SPINNING LIKE A TOP

Spinning is something that children love to do and it comes easily to them, but spinning as an adult can make some of us dizzy. Why is this? Well, it is because the inner ear has become hardened over time. The directional movement of the fluid in the inner ear causes dizziness. However, this Spinning exercise awakens the *nadis* around the ear, which can also improve hearing and balance.

• Find an open space that is quiet and safe. Stand with your legs shoulder-width apart.

• Breathe in, pulling the navel area back. Exhaling the breath, stretch your arms out wide to both sides.

• Turn your head right, and focus on the point at your middle finger. Start to turn slowly to the right. Increase your speed slowly to start the spinning motion. Keep moving in a circle to the right, while breathing easily. Keep your gaze at your middle finger to help ease the dizziness.

• Make a complete circle three times.

• Stop on the third completed spin, facing forward, and breathe in deeply.

• As you exhale, turn your gaze to your left hand. Keep your gaze at your middle finger to help ease the dizziness. Begin your spinning in the left direction for three rotations.

• Return to your starting position with your feet shoulder-width apart and your hands down at your side.

• Breathe and exhale three times, holding the position.

• Smile, you just were spinning like a child!

NOTE: Build up your spinning exercises very slowly. Up to 21 spins is recommended.

IT'S CRUNCH TIME

Option 1:

1.

2.

3.

4.

5.

Option 2:

1.

2.

3.

4.

5.

Tibetan Rite #2 –
IT'S CRUNCH TIME

This is an easy and ancient stomach crunch exercise that opens up the chest wall and releases trapped *rLung* energy. It also builds core strength.

• Begin by lying on your back with your arms relaxed at your sides and your legs fully extended, with your feet relaxed.

• Breathe in, gently pulling the navel area back, and exhale deeply, feeling the breath throughout your body.

• Inhale again, and while exhaling, simultaneously lift your head and knees up, bringing your knees into your stomach and gently wrapping your arms around your knees (not illustrated). Lift your head and shoulders up to meet them as best you can.

• Hold this position for one minute.

• Inhale and exhale again.

• Relax back, putting your head and shoulders down on the floor first, relax your legs in front of you.

• Repeat this three times.

End with lying flat on the mat and deeply exhaling.

NOTE: Build up your "crunching" exercises slowly. Up to 21 times is recommended in the ancient texts. For a more advanced version of the exercise (option 2), lift your straight legs up to 90 degrees while lifting your head off the ground at the same time.

LOOK UP/LOOK DOWN

1.

Tibetan Rite #3 – LOOK UP/LOOK DOWN

This is a kneeling position exercise that opens up the chest area. It is particularly beneficial for people with anxiety. It moves the *rLung* in the chest.

2.

• Begin by sitting in a kneeling position on the floor with the bottoms of your toes flexed against the floor for support (instead of putting the tops of your feet on the floor). Your heels should be touching each other. Place a pillow under your ankles if this position is painful at the beginning. You will build up this flexibility over time.

3.

• Place both of your hands behind you, on the back of your buttocks/top of sacrum area and keep them there throughout the exercise. Look upwards toward the sky, leading with your chin.

• Inhale deeply, pulling the navel area back gently.

4.

• As you exhale deeply, tuck your chin into your chest.

• Inhale deeply and look upwards toward the sky, leading with your chin.

• Exhale and slowly return your chin back to your chest, relaxing your shoulders and bringing your hands back to your sides.

5.

• Repeat one more time.

NOTE: The ancient texts always recommend 21 times for each exercise, but you can begin with just three of each.

THE CRAB

**Tibetan Rite # 4 -
THE CRAB**

This can be a strenuous exercise for some. Please go slowly, at your own pace. You will get more strength and flexibility with practice. This exercise connects all the vertical channels of the body, and opens up the middle of the body, bringing flow both up and down the main channel along your spine. This exercise is similar to "crab pose" in yoga.

• Start by sitting on the floor with your legs out in front of you and bend your knees. Your feet should be flat on the floor. Place your hands on the floor behind you with your fingers pointing towards your legs.

• Inhale slowly, prepare to move your body upwards. Exhale, move your stomach and hips upwards with your legs out in front of you and your heels on the floor. You will be in a position that is much like a table, with your stomach facing up and level with the floor, and your arms behind you. Relax your head and let it hang behind you and continue the deep breath slowly.

• Hold for one minute, breathing in and out as slowly as is comfortable.

• Simultaneously bring your head back in line with your spine and lower your hips slowly back to the floor with your knees bent and your arms behind you.

• Inhale in, pulling the navel area gently back, and then exhale fully.

• Inhale and repeat this movement for a total of three times.

NOTE: Start slowly and work up to 21 times at your own pace. Never push or force your body to do something that does not feel good.

UPWARD AND DOWNWARD DOG

1.

2.

3.

4.

5.

6.

7.

8.

Tibetan Rite #5 -
UPWARD AND DOWNWARD DOG

This is a strenuous exercise that should be done with care and mindfulness. The two primary positions are similar to the "upward dog" and "downward dog" positions in yoga.

• Lie on the floor, face down as if you are going to do a push up. Your hands should be under your shoulders.

• Pushing down with your arms, slowly arch your back and lift your chest up in the air, shifting your weight onto the balls of your feet and the palms of your hands, with your arms straight down in front of you. Your weight is equally supported on your hands and the balls of your feet. You'll have a curve in your back.

• Feeling secure in this position, breathe in. Your eyes should be looking forward and upwards in front of you. This is similar to the Upward Dog position in yoga.

• Exhale and slowly raise your bottom so that it is the highest part of your body. As you move into this higher position, breathe in and look forward and downward toward the floor. This is similar to the Downward Dog position in yoga.

• As you exhale, lower yourself down to the starting position, first by lowering your hips, then returning your arms to your side.

• Repeat three times.

NOTE: Work slowly up to 21 times, at your own pace.

POINTS TO PONDER
• The Tibetan Healing Exercises and Rites equalize the flow of *rLung* in the subtle channels in the body.
• The ancient theory behind these exercises is that they stimulate small energetic centers in your body, called the *nadis*.
See Chapter 7: The Flow of rLung for more information about the nadis.

Tibetan medicine's moxibustion is very good for *rLung* disorders and *Bad-gan* disorders, such as indigestion, lack of digestive heat, oedema, tumors, madness, dementia, and nerve disorders.

—*Dr. Tamdin Sither Bradley*
Principles of Tibetan Medicine
London: Singing Dragon Publications 2013

TWELVE

MOXIBUSTION FOR RELIEVING rLUNG

Moxibustion pre-dates acupuncture. At archaeological sites in China from the Shang Dynasty (1700–1100 BCE), hieroglyphs carved into bones and tortoise shells were found that show directions for applying moxibustion to points on the body. The moxibustion methods in Tibetan Medicine are similar to Mongolian methods, and both probably evolved simultaneously, due to strong trade links between the kingdoms.

The word moxibustion comes from the Japanese word, *mogusa* which means mugwort. Mugwort (*Artemesia vulgaris*) is the most common herb used for moxibustion. Today, many Western practitioners have shortened the word moxibustion to simply "moxa," but it is the same. Various herbs can be used in addition to mugwort. Tibetan doctors in the 1990's used Himalayan Edelweiss as the herb for moxibustion. It has since become a protected species, and doctors now use either Gerbera, from the sunflower family, using the dried roots and leaves, or mugwort, from the *Artemesia* genus, either *Artemesia vulgaris*, in the United States, or *Artemesia verlotiorum* in Asia.

opposite:
Dr. Jamling performing Golden Needle Moxibustion on a patient

149

Some practitioners call Mugwort "wormwood," which is an old name for it. Wormwood is also the name for *Artemesia absinthium*, which is an herb used to make the alcoholic drink absinthe, so it is not the most reliable term.

Tibetan medical doctors use moxibustion to relieve both the acute and chronic symptoms of *rLung* Imbalance. It warms, invigorates, and moves the *chi* or *rLung* energy. Moving the blocked *rLung* energy creates a smoother flow along the channels resulting in a smoother flow of thoughts, emotions, and even blood and bodily fluids for the person.

When someone comes into the clinic with anxiety, we immediately do moxibustion on the *rLung* points. It helps to control the flow of *rLung*, settling it into its proper channels. As discussed earlier in this book, the mind is very connected to the *rLung*, thus when the *rLung* energy is relaxed, the mind is relaxed, too. Apply moxibustion on the *rLung* points every day for three days, followed by every other day until the symptoms subside. Improvement usually happens immediately, but longer use is sometimes necessary with deeper *rLung* Imbalances.

The three most common methods of using moxibustion are:

• **Moxa stick**: The simplest method for moxibustion is to roll the herb in rice paper into the shape of a large cigar. This shape is called a moxa stick, which you then light and hold over an area of pain or a specific acu-point, bringing soothing and healing warmth to the area.

• **Cone moxa**: Some practitioners role the herb into tiny cones, light them with a match, and apply them directly to the skin, quickly removing them just before they burn the patient. It is a skilled process for the practitioner to acquire.

- **Moxa on top of a needle**: Another way acupuncturists use mugwort is to roll the herb into a ball and place the ball on the end of a needle and light it with a match. It infuses warmth from the herb into the body through the needle.

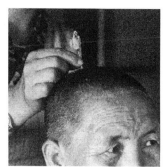

Whatever form of moxibustion is applied, the principles are the same. The heat encourages the *rLung* energy to come to these places and pools the *rLung* in the points where it belongs. The *rLung* scatters, disperses, and loses its home in *rLung*-related illnesses, and this practice mollifies the *rLung* and settles the patient.

Note: If you wish, you can apply a dab of warm sesame oil on the points before applying moxibustion to warm the points.

The *rLung* Moxibustion Points

Below is a diagram of various Tibetan Medicine points. The recommended set of *rLung* Moxibustion points to use for anxiety are shown on the next page.

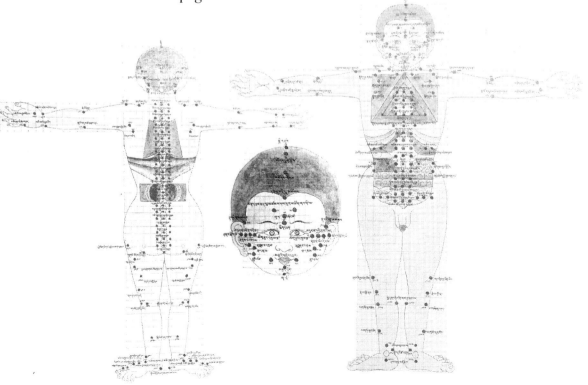

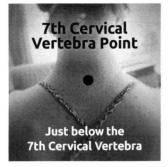

7th Cervical Vertebra Point
Just below the 7th Cervical Vertebra

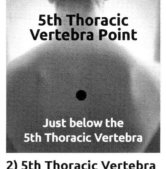

5th Thoracic Vertebra Point
Just below the 5th Thoracic Vertebra

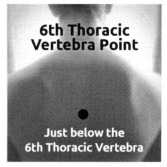

6th Thoracic Vertebra Point
Just below the 6th Thoracic Vertebra

1) The 7th Cervical Vertebra point: This is located in the vertebral space just below the 7th Cervical Vertebra. It is called Governing Vessel (GV) 14 in Chinese Medicine.

2) 5th Thoracic Vertebra point: This is located in the vertebral space just below the 5th Thoracic Vertebra. It is called GV 11 in Chinese Medicine.

3) 6th Thoracic Vertebra point: This is located in the vertebral space just below the 6th Thoracic vertebra. It is called GV 10 in Chinese Medicine. This point relates to the heart.

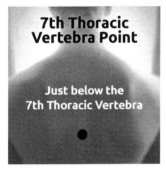

7th Thoracic Vertebra Point
Just below the 7th Thoracic Vertebra

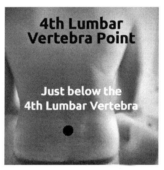

4th Lumbar Vertebra Point
Just below the 4th Lumbar Vertebra

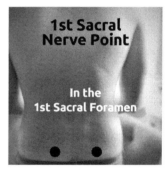

1st Sacral Nerve Point
In the 1st Sacral Foramen

4) 7th Thoracic Vertebra point: This is located in the vertebral space just below the 7th Thoracic vertebra. It is called GV 9 in Chinese Medicine. This point relates to the Life/Conception Vessel (CV) on the front of the body.

5) 4th Lumbar Vertebra point: This is located in the vertebral space just below the 4th Lumbar vertebra. This point relates to the large intestine. It is called GV 3 in Chinese Medicine. It's also connected to the Life/Conception Vessel on the front.

6) 1st Sacral Nerve point: This is located in the first sacral foramen on both sides the sacrum. It is called Bladder 27 in Chinese Medicine.

1) The Gladiolus Sternum point: On the center of the chest in between the nipples on the mid-line. It is called CV 17 in Chinese Medicine.

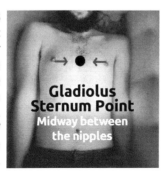

Gladiolus Sternum Point
Midway between the nipples

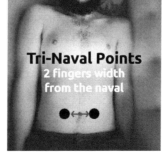

Tri-Naval Points
2 fingers width from the naval

2) The Tri-Navel points: On either side of the navel, two finger widths lateral on each side of the navel. It is called Stomach (ST) 25 in Chinese Medicine.

(Moxa) Stick to the Basics

Moxa sticks are commonly sold at acupuncture supply stores. They are burned over areas of the body and specific points and can produce a lot of smoke. If you are uncomfortable with smoke or fire, it is not recommended that you do this one your own. You can consult a Tibetan Medicine practitioner.

You can purchase moxa sticks or easily make them on your own. You'll need dried mugwort, rice paper, and a large plate.

1. Put the dried mugwort, rice paper, and large plate in front of you.
2. Take one square of rice paper and lay it flat.
3. Place the mugwort inside the square in a line along the edge of the paper closest to you.
4. Fold that edge over the mugwort and continue rolling until it approaches the shape of a tightly wound cigar.

5. Twist the ends to secure the herb.
6. Cut the cigar shape in half so you have two sticks.

You can use your moxa sticks on the *rLung* moxibustion points, as described below:

1. Find a quiet place where the patient can lie down or sit comfortably on a stool without a back while receiving moxibustion.
2. Have some matches, a large plate, a bowl of water (for quickly snuffing out the moxa flame if necessary), and scissors (for cutting the rolled moxa in half). Keep the moxa point diagrams in this book nearby, so you can see the points on the front and back of the body while you work.

3. Take care to light the stick over a bowl of water because the twisted paper on the end will fall off after it is lit.

4. After the twisted paper has fallen off the end, roll the end of the moxa stick in an ashtray so that the ember is even and tight.

5. First feel the point under your hand, and relax it with simple acupressure movements, massaging the point so that the heat does not come as a shock.

6. Hold the lit moxa stick stick just over the *rLung* moxibustion points **(not actually touching the skin)**. Follow the point on the chart, beginning with the points on the person's back.

7. When applying the moxa stick just over the points, use a slight pecking of the hand motion.

8. The pecking motion is easy: with a relaxed focus just slowly

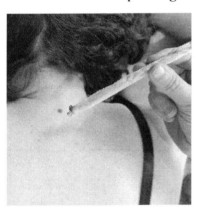

approach the point with the lit end of the moxa stick. Then pull back just before the stick reaches the surface of the skin.

9. Continue to do this several times.

10. As you do this, ask the person to tell you when the heat gets uncomfortable.

11. Continue the pecking motion until discomfort from the heat is reached.

12. Then move on to the next *rLung* point down the back.

13. Continue to the front *rLung* points after completing the ones on the back.

Cone Moxibustion

Cone moxibustion allows you to apply direct heat to the points. To make moxa cones, follow the instructions below:

1. Take a wad of mugwort into the palm of your hand, so that your palm contains about a two-inch diameter of the herb. This piece will easily squeeze into a rolled cone that is about a quarter of an inch in diameter.

2. With your other hand, begin to roll the mugwort into a ball.

3. Then take this ball with your thumb and forefinger and place it on a flat surface.

4. Hold the moxa ball and twist it in your fingers, gradually forming a cone.

5. Once the mugwort is in cone form, place it to the side.

6. You will need to make 20 cones in total for the *rLung* moxibustion points.

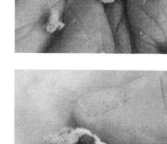

Once you're ready, have the moxa cones, some matches, a bowl of water, and your *rLung* moxa point diagrams ready at your side, and apply them as described below:

1. Ask the person to lie face down.

2. Start by placing a moxa cone directly on the first point, which is on the back, and light it. Do the moxibustion points in the order listed. You will be working your way down the back *rLung* points first.

3. Ask the person to tell you as soon as they begin to feel the heat.

4. When the person starts to feel the heat, quickly pull the cone away, and place it in the water. Be careful and mindful of the person's safety.

5. Place the next cone on the same point and repeat the same process. Each point gets two cone moxibustion treatments.

6. Next move onto the next point from the moxibustion diagrams.

7. When you have completed the back points, you can ask the person to turn over and begin on the front moxa points, also working down the body (CV 17 first then ST 25).

Note: For points that are located on both the left and right sides of the body, it doesn't matter which side you do first.

The Golden Needle Moxibustion Treatment

Golden Needle moxibustion is an acupuncture technique that uses a single point on top of the head. Tibetan Medicine typically uses acupressure instead of acupuncture. This is the only point that Tibetan Medicine doctors use for acupuncture. The point is called The Crown Point and is considered to be one of the most important points on the body. According to many Tibetan medical texts, it connects the microcosmic human self with the cosmos.

Golden needle moxibustion is an acupuncture technique that uses a single point on top of the head. The point is called The Crown Point and is considered to be one of the most important points on the body. According to many Tibetan medical texts, it connects the microcosmic human self with the cosmos.

Tibetan doctors usually perform the Golden Needle treatment while chanting the Medicine Buddha mantra. This mantra, which is also typically said every morning for patients, aligns practitioners with the spiritual history of their lineage. *See Chapter 8 for a description of the Medicine Buddha mantra.*

The Golden Needle treatment for *rLung* is to be done only after consultation with a Tibetan Medicine practitioner to ensure that the procedure and timing is correct. For example, this treatment is never done on a full moon, and depending on whether a patient is male or female, the moon time has to be corrected for this. The *rLung* flows in the channels clockwise for females, and counterclockwise for males.

A skilled practitioner may perform a Golden Needle moxibustion treatment in the following manner:

Apex Point (1)

Located at the top of the head

1. Take a small one-inch diameter of mugwort, and roll it into a ball. Have two other balls available.
2. To find the point on top of the head, take two pieces of string. With the first piece, find its beginning point by taking the patient's ear, and bending it in half. The halfway point on the ear is found, and here,

place the bottom half of the string. Pull the string to the top of the head and continue to bring it down to the same halfway point on the ear on the other side. Leave the string there for now. Then, take the second string, and measure from the tip of the nose, reaching up until the string crosses the first string. This is the location of the point. This point is called GV 20 in Chinese Medicine.

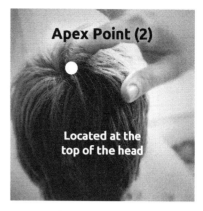

Apex Point (2)

Located at the top of the head

3. Then, take a needle made out of gold. Wipe the point with alcohol. Gently insert the needle.
4. Place the mugwort on top of the needle and light it, while saying the Medicine Buddha mantra. *See Chapter 8 for the Medicine Buddha mantra words and translation.*

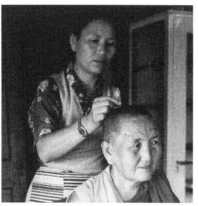

Dr. Jamling doing the Golden Needle Moxibustion technique

POINTS TO PONDER

- Moxibustion is a technique that warms, invigorates, and moves the *chi* or *rLung* energy.
- Moxibustion moves blocked *rLung* energy and creates a smoother flow along the channels resulting in a smoother flow of thoughts, emotions, and even blood and bodily fluids for the person.

I think the way forward for the world, one that
will bring the path of outer development in
harmony with the real root of happiness,
is that we allow the information that we
have to really make a change in our heart.

—*His Holiness the 17th Gyalwang Karmapa*

THIRTEEN

PUTTING IT ALL TOGETHER
YOUR NEW LIFESTYLE AND RETREAT GUIDE

Now that you have these tools—recipes, incense, massage, moxibustion, meditations, and exercises—you're ready to make space for your own personal healing journey. What practices in this book appealed to you? How would you embark on your journey, and what tools do you want in your "toolbox" to cope with your anxiety in a new way? In this chapter, we will discuss how to incorporate these new techniques in your daily life as well as into longer retreats you can do if you choose.

Creating Intention for a New Lifestyle

First, gather and order any supplies you may need and create a healing corner, shelf, or basket where you can keep all your supplies for a weekly or monthly tune-up. That way, all your supplies are handy, and you can quickly put together a nice evening of massage, moxibustion, and using the *rLung* incense.

One of my best friends, Pema-la, lives in McLeod Ganj in a three-room home with her uncle and aunt. I loved visiting them. It was tiny, and yet it was one of the homiest atmospheres I have ever experienced. Uncle slept on the couch at night, but in the day he was usually out and about. We would sit and have *chai*, Pema-la and I, and she would insist on helping me to work on my Tibetan language skills. Like most Tibetan homes, there was an altar with photos of His Holiness the Dalai Lama and other special teachers on it, as well as photos of deceased ancestors or children.

And there was also a shelf that had all the supplies for moxibustion, massage, and healing. Just like having first-aid kits, Tibetans have their shelf of supplies for home healing. All the practices in this book are familiar to Tibetans. Pema-la, for example, has grown up with her grandmother and her aunt making special bone soup for her if she suffers from stress or is debilitated after a long fever.

Create a healing corner, shelf, or basket to bring intention to your healing journey and give easy access to your new tools.

Your Supplies

On this shelf you will have all the basic supplies for doing warm oil massage, making herbal compresses, and doing moxibustion. You could also have this book, and other reference manuals for undertaking massage or acupressure there too. On the wall you could hang the Medicine Buddha Mantra. I have created one for you on our website if you would like to download it (*http://HealingAnxietyBook.com/Mantra*) or you can make one by hand. When we make a beautiful spot for ourselves that devotes energy to taking care of ourselves, we create a strong intention that strengthens our will and our resolve to be balanced in our lives.

You will need:

- Sesame oil
- Loose rags to wipe off the excess oil at the end of the massage
- A bowl to hold the warmed oil during massage
- Muslin sheets to make the compresses, cut into 4-inch square pieces or so

- Fennel, coriander, and nutmeg for making the warm compresses (*see Chapter 10 to review how to do the massage techniques*)
- Moxibustion sticks already prepared or purchased
- Loose Mugwort (*Artemesia vulgaris*) for making moxa cones (*see Chapter 12 to review how to do moxibustion*)
- The *rLung* incense (*see Resources for how to order the incense*)
- A jar with rice or sand in it, in which you can stand up the incense stick, and light it when you need it

Once you've put together your healing corner, shelf, or basket where all your supplies are, find yourself a nice journal. You can begin by writing down all that you want to shift in your life. What specifically would you like to feel, be, or do as a result of reducing your own personal anxiety? As you begin your new journey with Tibetan Medicine, use this journal to reflect on how you are progressing. Your initial entry will be a great touchstone to see your progress as you begin to feel better. Write like no one will ever read this but you. Be free and clear.

Adding these new techniques into your life takes some time. It's best to start simply.

- Begin with meditation. You can meditate in the morning for twenty minutes, then record in your journal how you felt. Did you feel relaxed? How did the meditation go? Write both the easy and the challenging parts down.
- You can also just keep track of what foods you are eating, and then see if they suit your constitution. Think about what you're eating and what you want to be eating to match your constitution.
- At night, start to develop a plan for the upcoming next day or even week. For example, you may decide to cut down on coffee, do the Tibetan healing exercises in the evening, and burn the *rLung* incense as you do the exercises.

Remember: the diet, meditation, *rLung* incense, and exercises really work, but only if you use them! Here is what Josephine said to me, when I asked how she incorporated these strategies into her daily life.

> I still have days when I wake up and feel a sense of doom that I can't name. But they are very few and far between. Then if I look at what I've been doing the last few weeks, I can see that I have been acting imbalanced—too rushed, eating bad food, and drinking too much alcohol and coffee. So then I will get my incense out, start meditating, make simple nutritious meals, and slow down . . . Often that is a sign for me to also do a longer retreat . . . Other things work for me, too. Instead of a cocktail in the evening, or a soda, I will have a relaxing cup of chamomile tea or lemon balm. But for me, it's really the diet and meditation that will nip the anxiety in the bud.

Here is another example: Nathan, a yoga teacher, can sometimes become *rLung* Imbalanced because his yoga practice is very successful, which causes him to sometimes over-exercise. For Nathan, he uses Tibetan Medicine meditations for anxiety and emphasizes slowing down. His diet is impeccable, so he doesn't have to change or work on improving that part of his lifestyle. This is how Nathan copes if he feels a wave of anxiety coming on:

> Well, so I'm running a super successful business. It's yoga, for sure—very pure and a great practice, but it's still a business! Ask any business owner if they have stress and anxiety. I bet they do! So because I'm incredibly busy, sometimes doing four classes in one day that start with waking up at 5:00 a.m., then in the afternoon doing admin—for me the Tibetan medical advice that works are the meditations and just slowing down. The best for me is to reboot every spring. I do a week,

maybe ten day or thirteen day retreat, and that helps me for the whole year. The Tibetan healing exercises are phenomenal, as well.

For me personally, I have been meditating steadily since I first became anxious and was healed with this simple Tibetan medical advice. The meditation and following my own *Bad-Gan/Tipa* combination diet keeps me completely balanced most of the time. I haven't had any anxiety since the late 1990s! I also burn the Tibetan healing *rLung* incense almost every day as I meditate. I try to get massage at least once per month, usually from my husband using our special Tibetan massage oil and compresses. I also walk 45 minutes every morning, breathing in the fresh air, and getting some movement and calmness from being outdoors. Thus, what I use from my own personal anxiety toolbox is daily meditatations, *rLung* incense, massage, diet, and exercise. The Tibetan healing exercises are a rare treat, and I do love them. Every year, my husband and I do an extended healing retreat, and it reboots us for the year.

Taking a Retreat

The purpose of a retreat is to take time to quiet your mind, settle the *rLung*, and heal your body so it can detox and renew. Taking a retreat does more than just allow you to have time to learn how to do these techniques to ease anxiety. Consider finding or creating your own retreat for a way to jumpstart your new lifestyle. It's a chance to completely unplug from the world. A retreat will help you breathe in new life and savor the cleansing process of the right foods for your constitution. You'll spend time with just yourself, or a partner, and focus on taking care of yourself.

The most economical way to do a retreat is to stay home, rather than finding some retreat spa that won't have this book available for properly harnessing the *rLung*! If you have the resources available, renting a house or vacation spot is also a great way to have a retreat, and it helps you get away from the temptations of housework and other daily life rituals that can distract you during the retreat. Ask friends or family to join you, or simply do some research online to find a retreat that suits you.

It may seem like a lot, but I recommend a thirteen-day retreat. Thirteen days! You may not be able to take the whole thirteen days off work. If an extended thirteen-day retreat won't fit into your life right now, think about a seven-day retreat, with time on both ends to prepare and finish, gently easing back into the work world. Do three days, if life is that busy. Be gentle on yourself.

I think that sincere motivation is very important for our future well-being, our deep sense of wellbeing as humans, and I think that means sinking into whatever it is you're doing now. Whatever work you're doing now to benefit the world, sink into that, get a full taste of that.

We often miss the very subtle changes, and I think that sometimes we develop grand concepts of what happiness might look like for us. But if we pay attention we can see that there are little symbols of happiness in every breath we take.

—His Holiness the 17th Gyalwang Karmapa

PREPARING FOR YOUR THIRTEEN-DAY RETREAT

You want to get your mind around the idea of really unplugging from the world. During this retreat, you'll want to get plenty of rest. You will turn off your computer and phone, even giving them to a next-door neighbor if needed, so you are not tempted. To get the most out of this time with yourself, you want to avoid any strenuous exercise, sexual activity, late nights and watching television, or listening to loud music.

Hopefully, your environment is conducive to creating a quiet atmosphere. A small amount of relaxing music can be beneficial, as can candles, atmospheric incense, and essential oils. Wear loose-fitting, comfortable clothing. Sleep in simple cotton sheets, and avoid using a fan if possible, unless you are a strongly overheated *Tipa* type!

This is a very special time for you—a rare opportunity to go within yourself and detox, reboot your system, and cherish and respect the *rLung* energy that keeps you alive. So to truly benefit from this time, think about maintaining a calm atmosphere. Use this time to do some journaling, drawing, or reading of uplifting literature instead of being on the Internet or in front of a TV screen. Do all your chores before beginning the retreat, such as paying bills, returning phone calls, cleaning out that closet, or doing the laundry. Buy all your groceries beforehand, and try to arrange your life so that you're simply being at home, with simple cooking and light cleaning. Outdoor time is also important. Plan to take some walks, breathing in fresh air, and sit in a garden if the weather is warm enough. Perhaps a small touch of gardening, but nothing strenuous is to be done. Embrace nature.

If you have a partner, support one another in the process of preparing for your retreat time together. During the retreat, keep voices to a minimum, and keep in mind that this is only thirteen days out of perhaps the whole year that you have this time to cherish your health in this simple yet sacred way. Almost every summer my husband and I do this retreat, although we have done variations from other traditions, as well. At the end of our summer detox retreat, we are always astounded at how alert we have become, how our eyesight has improved, and how we sleep better. I come out of our summer retreat less hungry, more grounded, and with more energy. I'm more relaxed, too. These retreats help us to realign our system, balance our Humors, and also loosen great amounts of stuck emotions and shed emotional clutter. We feel much more pure of heart and mind and body.

SHOPPING FOR YOUR RECIPES: *rLUNG* BALANCING FOODS AND YOUR CONSTITUTION

For thirteen days you will be eating mainly kitchari, which balances all three humors, but especially *rLung*. Kitchari is a wonderful grain and legume dish made with mung beans and basmati rice. It's spiced with cumin, coriander, salt, and black pepper. Your largest meal will be in the middle of the day and will consist of a large bowl

Kitchari with garnishes for each Humor: Shitake mushrooms (*rLung*), sliced cucumbers (*Tipa*), and hot peppers (*Bad-Gan*).

of kitchari. Each person can modify the kitchari so that it suits their constitution. For example, a *Bad-Gan* person can add ginger and grated red pepper, a *Tipa* person can add cold shredded cucumbers or other cooling vegetables as a garnish. And a *rLung* type can add some nutritious meats, in small amounts, on top.

Retreat Grocery List:
- Basmati rice
- Mung beans
- Ghee
- Ground cumin
- Ground coriander
- Salt
- Black pepper
- Chamomile tea
- Fennel tea
- Sesame oil for massage

SHOPPING FOR YOUR CONSTITUTION

Eating kitchari for thirteen days can be a struggle for many people. The simple diet of kitchari has a cleansing effect on the colon, helps to flush out toxins, and soothes inflammation that may have been built up in the system due to *rLung* Imbalance. It also gives our poor stomachs a break. They've been working hard our whole lives. On about day three I always wake up longing for a hamburger, a nice grilled piece of salmon, or a slice of pecan pie! After three days on the simple kitchari diet, we turn to adding small amounts of food on top that suit our constitution. That way, we get the grounded, balanced, pure dietary support for *rLung* through the kitchari, and support for our constitutional type through the garnish on top.

Tipa Garnish Grocery List:
- Almonds
- Coriander leaves (cilantro)
- Small amounts of free-range, grass-fed chicken
- Fresh-water fish
- Shrimp
- Yogurt
- Tofu
- Parsley
- Cucumber
- Peas
- Radishes
- Summer squash
- Lettuce
- Okra
- Broccoli
- Brussels sprouts
- Cabbage
- Dandelion greens
- Any sweet fruits such as apples, apricots, avocado, berries, dates, figs, mangoes, oranges

Bad-Gan Garnish Grocery List:

The *Bad-Gan* constitution runs cold. So the foods listed here, as we talked about before, warm *Bad-Gan* types. It gets their digestive juices flowing and the blood circulating through their body. They feel they have more energy, and their sluggish digestion speeds up. You will follow the kitchari diet for the thirteen days, but after three days you can garnish and spice up the mixture. In the morning you can have a small bowl of non-fat yogurt with chia seeds and some of the bitter fruits listed here. This list just gives you an idea of how to spice it up. You won't need all of these foods—just get the ones you like.

- Apples, apricots, applesauce, berries, cherries, cranberries, or pomegranates
- Artichoke
- Asparagus
- Beet greens (the tops of beets)
- Beets
- Bitter melon
- Broccoli
- Brussels sprouts
- Burdock root
- Cabbage
- Celery
- Cilantro
- Corn
- Daikon radish
- Dandelion greens
- Eggplant
- Fennel
- Green chilies
- Horseradish
- Kale
- Kohlrabi
- Oat bran
- Buttermilk

- Non-fat yogurt
- Soy milk
- Black pepper, chili pepper, mustard—all hot spices to increase digestive fire
- Chia seeds
- Flax seeds

NOTE: *Nuts are not on the Bad-Gan shopping list.*

rLung Garnish Grocery List:

Since we are following a retreat for healing anxiety and *rLung* Imbalance, the *rLung* constitution person is well supported for the thirteen days, especially with the basic kitchari recipe, which grounds the *rLung* energy. However, everyone, after the first three days of pure kitchari, likes to add some refreshing flavors. You can do this without destroying the purity of the kitchari and while continuing the detoxification and fast. So for *rLung* types, the foods to add on top of the kitchari would be of a very nutritious and moisturizing nature.

- Apricots
- Avocado
- Bananas
- Dates
- Figs
- Kiwi
- Mangoes
- Lemons
- Limes
- Oranges
- Papaya
- Peaches
- Plums
- Strawberries
- Asparagus
- Beets

- Cabbage
- Cauliflower
- Cilantro
- Cucumber
- Fennel
- Green beans
- Leafy greens (wilted)
- Okra
- Olives (black)
- Sweet potatoes or yams
- Oats
- Butter
- Buttermilk
- Yogurt
- Almost any meat: except no pork
- Chia seeds
- Flax seeds
- Sesame seeds
- Sunflower seeds

 Tip: Now that you have all the groceries, you might want to make the first three days' worth of kitchari in advance, so it's ready to warm up and eat at mealtimes.

PREPARING YOUR BODY AND MIND: THE FIRST THREE DAYS

In 1991 in Dharamsala, I embarked on my first retreat. I dissapeared from the world into the folds of a small and safe monastery. I kept a journal and here are some of my thoughts from that time in my life. I combined my journaling with daily walking, meditation, massage, and the kitchari served most days during our meditation retreat. It was three hours of meditation per day, one hour of massage, simple chores, and much time for reflection. I expected from this experience to feel deep calmness, elation, and purity of spirit!

Little did I know that unplugging from the world, calming down the senses, calming the nervous system, and detoxifying my body was actually hard work. Day one through three felt tiring and draining. I found I was sleeping more. I felt foggy-headed and a bit irritable. This was the process of my body finally having a free moment to get rid of toxins that had been building up in my tissues. The brain fog was probably my lack of caffeine as well as mucous leaving my upper cavities and being sloughed off in the digestive tract. The fatigue had also a muscular quality to it: it was hard to do the chores required of us! I felt sluggish and lazy. After three days, this passed.

At this point, what I now know as mid-fast or mid-retreat awareness started to emerge. Suddenly I was sleeping less and had more energy. My meditative mind was more focused and yet calmer, too. I felt lighter. The mid-retreat awareness is fantastic. This clarity comes because we've moved out of the stage of coming off caffeine, sugar, etc. Doing massage also opens the channels so that all the toxins can come out and be properly flushed out of the body. The massage loosens and breaks up the toxins in the tissues, which then are released into the blood stream and lymph for removal. This process at first gives us the brain fog, fatigue, and discomfort, until the toxins are flushed away, and we are left with a mid-retreat joyous feeling.

For some people however, things get worse again, before they get finally better toward the end. Hang onto that mid-retreat high that gives you the strength to continue the exercises, meditations, diet, and massage. Toward the end, you might let go of some very deeply seated emotions, almost with no name. A sort of special deep breathing may show up in your meditations, or you shed a few tears for no reason. While receiving a massage you might laugh, groan deeply, or shiver while you let go of some deeply held muscular tension that finally found its way out of your body due to the many days of massage and care. It's a very special adventure.

So get ready! Here's what your day could look like.

MORNING ROUTINE

- Wake up with the sun if you can.
- Wash your face, brush your teeth.
- Sit quietly, and dedicate yourself to this day and to being of service to your health.
- Feel gratitude for the opportunity. Send healing and love out to the world.
- Prepare a cup of chamomile tea.
- While it steeps, do a ten-minute meditation, with the *rLung* incense burning.
- Eat breakfast according to your constitution.
- Walk outside and take in large, deep breaths of fresh air for 20 minutes.
- Do the Five Tibetan Rites, gently, not forcing yourself into the positions if they are too strenuous for you.
- Shower, remembering to avoid strong perfumes and soaps.

MID-DAY ROUTINE

- Receive massage and moxibustion. Either you can invite a massage therapist over each day, or do the retreat with a friend or partner, and alternate taking care of one another. If you are caring for one another, after you have given a massage, bathe lightly to refresh yourself.
- Eat lunch—your largest meal of the day. For the first three days, eat only pure kitchari. On the fourth day, you can add garnishes to the kitchari according to your constitution.
- Rest as long as you want or need. Drink warm water or chamomile tea throughout the day, remaining hydrated.
- Keep a journal of your thoughts, draw, or read lightly. Do not take too much exciting or stimulating material into yourself. Read poetry versus a detective story, for example. Feel free to listen to calming music that soothes.

EARLY EVENING

- Gather yourself up from your sedentary activity and begin to put away dishes and do preparations for dinner. Dinner will be simply a small bowl of kitchari heated up. After three days, you may add a garnish according to your constitution.

- Eat dinner. If you have water with dinner, make sure it is warm, and drink it toward the end of the meal. Do not stuff yourself. You want about one third of the stomach to be empty, giving plenty of room for digestion.

- After dinner, rest and meditate for 20 minutes with the *rLung* incense.

- After one hour has passed from dinner, do the Three Tibetan Healing Exercises. This will take you up to two hours. If this is challenging, please start with only very simple steps, doing the minimal amount, at the slowest pace you can. For example, you could do one or three head rolls to each side (but not two). These exercises open up the channels, the *nadis*, and allow the free flow of *rLung* energy healthily through the body. They are very calming. Feel free to play soft, calming music in the background as you do them.

- Afterwards, rest and drink hot water or tea. Make sure to drink plenty of fluids.

LATE EVENING

- If you haven't prepared the kitchari in advance, now is a good time to cook. *Note: I suggest preparing three days of kitchari at a time.* If you have someone bringing your food, and also doing house calls for massage, you are free now to rest, write, relax, meditate, or softly stretch. Take a relaxing bath.

- Go to bed when you are ready. Consider doing the body scan meditation as you are falling asleep. You can burn the *rLung* incense one more time, breathing in lightly the last calming fragrance before you drift off to sleep.

By day thirteen, you're probably hearing beautiful music in your mind as you awake in the morning with a feeling of freshness and vitality. You skip easily through the Five Tibetan Rites in the morning, and your body now knows when it is hungry and when it is full. You are no longer yearning after your computer or your phone, but instead, step outside and marvel at the fresh air and the moving, breathing trees. You are more in tune with nature. You will have many beautiful reflections; so keep your journal close beside you.

Day thirteen is also special because you get glimmerings of your other life coming back to you. You fall asleep with thoughts of going to work the next day or greeting your children. Perhaps you've got laundry that piled up, or you think about emails, messages, and returning to life.

As you move back into your old life, don't lose your serenity. When you wake up on the first day of normal life, you might have dreams of that roasted chicken you're going to prepare, or finally getting out, and having that special dinner party with friends you've put off.

When the retreat is done, bring your new self with you into normal life. Slowly introduce your old favorite foods. Breathe deeply. Think about continuing the parts of the retreat that stood out for you as special. For me, I continue to plunge into the morning with intention. It has now become part of my daily routine: I send out to the world my best thoughts, and I know they will come back to me. Introduce noise, computers, deadlines, fast food, and dinner parties slowly if you feel that need. Hold onto what you can from your sacred time. And think about honoring your constitution as much as you can.

The Future

When I think about Tibetan Medicine, I have such gratitude. To me, in my discovery of Tibet's healing culture, I felt as though East met West in my very own mind, in my brain, and my heart. I had found a lost self, and I wasn't going to let it go. Tibetan Medicine slowed me down, removed my anxiety, and returned me to my deeper self. In my small apothecary, filled with jars of organic, locally and domestically grown herbs, incense, and salves, I am thankful every day for this practice of medicine. It has returned me to a relationship with the earth that involves cultivating my own teas and vegetables in my garden. I go slowly, thoughtfully, through my day. And now I have brought you my simple understanding of one of the greatest healing traditions in the world.

Aum Tat! Sat! Aum!

I am thou, thou art I,

Parts of the Divine Self

ENDNOTES

PART I
Chapter 1:
1. (p. 3) – *rLung* is pronounced "loong" (the o sound and the n sound are drawn out a bit).

Chapter 2:
1. (p. 20) – Eaglewood 35 is a special herbal pill that is available online. *See Resources for additional information.*

Chapter 3:
1. (p. 36) – Nettles (*Urtica dioica*) grow wild throughout India and even in North America. They are stinging weeds found on the edges of hillsides and forests. They lose their stinging quality when they are soaked or cooked. They can be used in beef stew, added in at the last minute, as one would add spinach. In fact, nettles can replace spinach in any recipe.

2. (p. 40) – R.C. Kessler et al., "Prevalence, severity, and comorbidity of twelve-month DSM-IV disorders in the National Comorbidity Survey Replication," *Archives of General Psychiatry* 62, no.6 (2005): 617-27.

PART II
Chapter 6:
1. (p. 87) – © The Library of Tibetan Works and Archives, Dharamsala, India. With permission.

2. (p. 88) – Herbert Benson et al., "Body temperature changes during the practice of *gTum-mo yoga*," *Nature* 295, no. 5846 (1982): 234–236.

Chapter 8:

1. (p. 96) – From a lecture given by His Holiness The Dalai Lama of Tibet at the Kalmuck Mongolian Buddhist Center, New Jersey. Transcribed by Ngawang Tashi (Tsawa), Drepung Loseling, Mungod India, (http://www.sacred-texts.com/bud/tib/omph.htm).

2. (p. 97) – These are the Buddhas of the past, present, and future.

3. (p. 97) – *The Collected Works of Dilgo Khyentse*, Volume One. (Boston: Shamballa Publications, 2011).

Chapter 9:

1. (p. 115) – Long pepper (*Piper retrofractum* or *Piper longum*) is a Southeast Asian pepper with a hot and sweet taste.

Chapter 11:

1. (p. 133) Barbara King, *The Yogis of Tibet* (JEHM FILMS, USA, 2002), NTSC video, directed by Jeffrey M. Pill.

RESOURCES

TIBETAN MEDICINE SUPPLIES

Special *rLung* Incense
You can order *rLung* incense from The Tibetan Medical and Astro. Institute.

Ment-Tsee-Khang
Tibetan Medicine and Astro. Institute
Gangchen Kyishong
Dharmsala 176215
Dist. Kangra,
Himachal Pradesh, INDIA
www.men-tsee-khang.org

Dr. Jamling's incense can
also be purchased from
this monastery:
Tashi Choeling Monastery
Jogiwara Road
McLeod Ganj
Upper Dharamsala, 176219
Himachal Pradesh, INDIA

Moxa
You can order moxa sticks or mugwort online. There are many providers, but some require that you be a practitioner of Chinese Medicine. A good site is **Lhasa OMS** http://www.lhasaoms.com/

Herbal pills
You can obtain the herbal pill Eaglewood 35 mentioned in numerous treatments throughout this book from the Tibetan Medical and Astro. Institute.

178

Ment-Tsee-Khang
Tibetan Medicine and Astro. Institute
Gangchen Kyishong
Dharmsala 176215
Distt. Kangra,
Himachal Pradesh, INDIA
www.men-tsee-khang.org

It is a good idea to consult a Tibetan Medicine practitioner before taking them. *See the next page for a list of schools and practitioners.*

Massage Oil and Compresses
You can buy the massage oil and compresses at any Tibetan store around the world or from the Tibetan Medical and Astro. Institute.

Ment-Tsee-Khang
Tibetan Medicine and Astro. Institute
Gangchen Kyishong
Dharmsala 176215
Distt. Kangra,
Himachal Pradesh, INDIA
www.men-tsee-khang.org

TIBETAN MEDICINE RESOURCES WORLDWIDE

INDIA
Ment-Tsee-Khang
Tibetan Medicine and Astro. Institute
Gangchen Kyishong
Dharmsala 176215
Distt. Kangra,
Himachal Pradesh, INDIA
www.men-tsee-khang.org

Chagpori Tibetan Medical Institute
Trogawa House, North Point
Darjeeling 734 104
West Bengal, INDIA
Telephone: 00 91 354 70266
www.chagpori.org

BURYAT
**Center of Oriental Medicine and
The Buryat Scientific Center**
10 Linkhovoina St
Ulan-Ude
Buryatia 670000

AUSTRIA
**Information Center for
Tibetan Medicine**
Dr. Florian Uberall
Franz-Stockmayerstrasse 30a
A-6410 Telfs
http://www.florianueberall.at/

BELGIUM
Samye Dzong Brussels
Karma Gyamtso Shedrup Long
33 Rue Capouillet
1060 Brussels
www.samye.be

GERMANY
Institute for East-West Medicine
Mariannenweg 48
61348 Bad Homburg
www.ostwestmedizin.de/
ausbildung/

ITALY
**The New Yuthok Institute
for Tibetan Medicine**
Via marmorata 169, sc8 int.11
Roma 153
www.newyuthok.it/

Shang-Shung Institute
Casella Postade
IT-58031 Arcidosso
www.shangshunginstitute.ru/en/
ssi/branches/italy/

DENMARK
Tibet Herbal Clinic
Dr. Bhuti Losang
Erslevvej 15
2820
Gentofte, Denmark
Telephone: +45 397 66888
tibetclinic.dk/index.php/dk/

NETHERLANDS
**Praktijk voor Tibetaanse
Geneeskunde**
Amchi Lobsang Tsultrim
De Gasperisingel 18
NL-6716 RB Ede
http://www.amchilobsang.com/

SWEDEN
**Svenske Tibetanska Skol-och
Kulturforeningen**
Dr. Tamdin S. Bradley and
Dr. Bhuti Losang
Allhelgonogatan 5 o.g.
11858 Stockholm
+46 8 643 4947
www.tibet-school.org/

SWITZERLAND
Padma, Inc
Tibetan Herbal
Medicine Formulas
Weisenstrasse 5
CH-8603 Schwerzenbach
www.padma.ch

Project Tibetan Medical and
Astro. Institute, Mount Kailash
Tsering Batsang
See-Strasse 94
CH-8810 Horgen
www.kailashprojekte.ch/tmai-
health.htm

UNITED KINGDOM
Kailash Centre of
Oriental Medicine
Dr. Tamdin S. Bradley
7 Newcourt St
London NW8 7AA
www.kailashcentre.org/tam-
din-bradley.html

United Kingdom Shang Shung
Institute
10a Chalcot Gardens
London
NW3 4YB
www.shangshunguk.org/

UNITED STATES
Alternative Medicine Foundation
PO Box 60016
Potomac, MD 20859
www.amfoundation.org

The Nyerongsha Institute
Dr. Dickey P. Nyerangsha
1200 Keith Avenue
Berkeley, CA 94708
www.clavan.net/

UCLA Department of Psychiatry
and Biobehavioral Sciences
Dr. Lobsang Rabgay
300 Medical Plaza, Suite 2331
Los Angeles, CA 90095
www.international.ucla.edu/
buddhist/person/275

Traditional Tibetan Healing
Dr. Keyzom Bhuti
689 Somerville Ave. #3
Somerville, MA 02143
www.tibetanherbalhealing.com

Shang Shung Institute Medical
School
PO Box 277
18 Schoolhouse Road
Conway, MA 01341
www.shangshung.org

Meridian Medical Group
Dr. Choyang Phuntsok
102 E. 30th St.
New York, NY 10016
www.meridianmedical.org/

Tibetan Medicine and
Holistic Healing Clinic
2955 Valmont Rd., Suite 100
Boulder, CO 80301
www.holistic-health.org

ONLINE RESOURCES
Tibetan Medicine
Education Center
www.tibetanmedicine-edu.org/

The Tibetan and Himalayan
Digital Library
www.thdl.org

MBSR
http:/news.harvard.edu/gazette/
tag/mindfulness-based-stress-
reduction-mbsr-program/

CHAPTER QUOTATIONS

Part I: His Holiness the Dalai Lama, from his forward to *Thoughts without a Thinker*, by Mark Esptein. New York: Basic Books, 1995.

Chapter 1: Dr. (Lady) Dadhon Jamling

Chapter 2: Dr. (Lady) Dadhon Jamling

Chapter 3: Dr. (Lady) Dadhon Jamling

Chapter 4: from the *Dhammapada, Sayings of the Buddha*, edited by Thomas Byrom. Shambhala Publications: Boston and London, 1993.

Chapter 5: His Holiness the Dalai Lama, from his forward to *Tibetan Buddhist Medicine and Psychiatry: The Diamond Healing*, by Terry Clifford. New York: Samuel Weiser, 1984.

Part II: Padmasambhava from the 8th Century, from *Way of the White Clouds*, by Anagarika Govinda. New York: Overlook Press 1995.

Chapter 6: Dr. (Lady) Dadhon Jamling

Chapter 7: Dr. Nyima Tsering, from *Illuminating rLung: The Vital Energy of Tibetan Medicine*, by Alma Rominger, SIT Study Abroad. Boston: Tufts University, 2013.

Chapter 8: His Holiness the Dalai Lama, from his "Tibetan Medical Center Opening Speech," 1991.

Chapter 9: Dr. Yeshe Donden. *Healing from the Source: The Science and Lore of Tibetan Medicine*. Ithaca, NY: Snow Lion Publications, 2000.

Chapter 10: Dr. (Lady) Dadhon Jamling

Chapter 11: Christopher Kilham, from *Inner Power: Secrets from Tibetan and the Orient*. New York and Tokyo: Japan Publications, 1981.

Chapter 12: Dr. (Lady) Dadhon Jamling

Chapter 13: His Holiness the 17th Gyalwang Karmapa at TEDIndia 2009.

BIBLIOGRAPHY

Birnbaum, Raoul. *The Healing Buddha.* Boston: Shambala Publications, 1979.

Cayton, Amy, ed. *Balanced Mind, Balanced Body: Anecdotes and Advice from Tibetan Buddhist Practitioners on Wind Disease.* Portland, OR: Foundation for the Preservation of the Mahayana Tradition, 2007.

Clark, Barry, trans. *The Quintessence Tantras of Tibetan Medicine.* Boston: Snow Lion Publications, 1995.

Clifford, Terry. *Tibetan Buddhist Medicine and Psychiatry: The Diamond Healing.* New York: Samuel Weiser, 1984.

Dalai Lama. *How to Practice: The Way to a Meaningful Life.* New York: Pocket Books, 2002.

Dilgo, Khyentse. *The Collected Works of Dilgo Khyentse.* Boston and London: Shambhala, 2010.

Donden, Yeshe. *Health Through Balance: An Introduction to Tibetan Medicine.* Ithaca, NY: Snow Lion Publications, 1986.

Donden, Yeshe. *Healing from the Source: The Science and Lore of Tibetan Medicine.* Ithaca, NY: Snow Lion Publications, 2000.

Dorjee, Pema with Janet Jones and Terence Moore. *Heal Your Spirit, Heal Yourself: The Spiritual Medicine of Tibet.* London: Watkins Publishing, 2012.

Dummer, Thomas. *Tibetan Medicine and Other Holistic Healthcare Systems.* New Delhi, India: Paljor Publications, 2001.

Finkh, Elizabeth. *Foundations of Tibetan Medicine,* Vols 1-3. London: Watkins Press, 1988.

Kilham, Christopher. *Inner Power: Secrets of Tibet and the Orient* Tokyo: Japan Publications, 1988.

Namdul, Tenzin, ed. *Tibetan Medical Dietary Book,* Vol. 1. Dharamsala, India: Ment-Zee Khang, Clinical Research Press, 2006.

Norbu, Chogyal Namkai. *The Practice of Kunye Massage.* Italy and Conway, MA: Shang Shung Editions, 2003.

Tsarong, T.J. and Tibetan Medical & Astro. Institute. *Fundamentals of Tibetan Medicine.* New Delhi, India: Paljor Publications, 2002.

GLOSSARY OF TERMS

Aloeswood – one ingredient used in the making of special *rLung* incense. Aloeswood is an aromatic resin wood from the *Aquilaria* trees. It's native to Southeast Asia.

Anger – the emotion that gives rise to the Humor Bile (*Tipa*).

Aquilaria – a tree that is native to Southeast Asia. *Aquilaria* is one ingredient used in the making of special *rLung* incense. Aloeswood is another name for the resinous wood from this tree.

Artemesia absinthium – the herb used to make the alcoholic drink absinthe, sometimes called Wormwood.

Artemisia vulgaris – an herb called mugwort. This herb is used in moxibustion (*see moxibustion below*).

Aruna fruit – the fruit that the Medicine Buddha holds in his hand, as shown on the cover of this book.

Asofoetida – a spice that is one ingredient used in making the special *rLung* incense.

Bad-Gan (Phlegm) – one of the Three Humors of the body. It represents cold in the body and aids many functions of the body, including digestion, mental stability, the health of joints, and the strength of our bodies' structure. Also spelled *Bad-Kan* in some translations.

bDag-zin – what Buddha called desire or Ego. It differentiates into the three basic emotions that give rise to the Three Humors: ignorance, anger, and desire.

Bile (Tipa) – one of the three humors of the body that represents heat. It helps regulate the temperature of the body, the ability to strategize and discriminate, metabolic functions, and the liver. Also spelled *mKhris-pa* in many translations.

Bodhicitta – to make the decision to gain enlightenment, not just for oneself, but for all beings who are suffering. A *Boddhisatva* is a person who has generated *Bodhicitta*.

Canella – a plant that is similar to cinnamon and is often called Wild Cinnamon.

Chi or Qi - Chi is energy. This energy circulates inside the body along meridian lines or channels. Chi is also present in every aspect of the cosmos.

Constitution - a person's general makeup that includes a set of attributes and tendancies.

Desire - the emotion that gives rise to the Humor Wind (*rLung*).

Edelweiss (*Leontopodium alpinum*) - Tibetan doctors in the 1990s used Himalayan edelweiss as the herb for moxibustion. It has since become a protected species.

Elements - The Five Elements describe the energetic nature of all things.

Gerbera - a plant that was used instead of mugwort for moxibustion. It comes from the sunflower family. Practitioners used the dried roots and leaves.

Ghee - clarified butter, which you can make by cooking butter until it separates and then straining out the milkfat and keeping the clear layer between the milk solids on the bottom of the pan and the foam on top.

rGyud-bzhi - (pronounced gyu-shee) the main Tibetan medical text called *The Four Tantras*, which is over a thousand years old.

Horgyi-metsa - the Tibetan word for moxibustion (*see moxibustion below*).

Humors - the three vital substances of the body: *rLung, Tipa,* and *Bad-Gan.*

Ignorance - the emotion that gives rise to the humor Phlegm (*Bad-Gan*).

Kitchari - a type of dish that usually is a mix of grains and legumes. *See the* Healing Anxiety *recipe for Kitchari in Chapter 9.*

Kundalini - a type of yoga and is also the word for a type of energy in the body.

rLung (Wind) - one of the Three Humors. It represents circulation in the body, such as circulation of blood and energy. It is also responsible for the circulation of thoughts in the mind.

MBSR - Mindfulness Based Stress Reduction is a meditation program designed to help people with pain and life issues. *See Resources for more information.*

Medicine Buddha - the *Bhaisajyaguru* is the formal name for the Medicine Buddha, who is the buddha of healing and medicine. The Medicine Buddha cures suffering.

Mogusa - Japanese word for mugwort (*see below*).

Moxibustion (Horgyi-metsa) - the technique of burning a special herb (typically *Artemisia vulgaris*) on or near the skin, especially on acu-points.

Mugwort - wormwood from the *Artemesia genus*, either *Artemesia vulgaris*, in the United Sates, or *Artemesia verlotiorum*, in Asia, but not *Artemesia absinthium*.

Myrobalan - a type of fruit-bearing tree, such as cherry plum. Myrobalan is one ingredient used in making the special *rLung* incense and is a common herb used in Asian medicine.

Nadis - the Tibetan word for meridians or channels through which energy of *chi/qi* flows.

Nagarjuna - one of the foremost medical doctors in Tibetan Medicine and the founder of one of the largest schools of Buddhism in the world. Nagarjuna wrote the seminal text on herbal medicine entitled, *The One Hundred Prescriptions*, and he also wrote, *The Precious Collection*, a gathering of medical advice and prescriptions. He, along with other Buddhist monk scholars, helped advance the practice of Tibetan Medicine greatly.

Nettles - a plant that grows wild throughout India and even in North America (*Urtica dioica*). They are a stinging weed found on the edges of hillsides and forests, which, once cooked or made into tea, are edible and can be beneficial.

Om Mani Padme Hum - a meditation chant.

Phlegm (*Bad-Gan*) - one of the Three Humors of the body. It represents cold in the body and aids many functions of the body, including digestion, mental stability, the health of joints, and the strength of our bodies' structure. Also spelled *Bad-Kan* in some translations.

PTSD - Post Traumatic Stress Disorder is a mental health condition that causes severe anxiety and flashbacks of past stressful events in a person's life.

Puja - prayers.

***rLung* (Wind)** - one of the Three Humors. It represents circulation in the body, such as circulation of blood and energy. It is also responsible for the circulation of thoughts in the mind.

Roseroot (*Rhodiola rosea*) - a perennial flowering plant that is one ingredient used in making the special *rLung* incense. It promotes endurance and increases longevity.

Shakyamuni Buddha - Buddha (or as the Tibetans refer to him, Shakyamuni Buddha—the Great Physician).

srog-rLung - (pronounced sok loong), a kind of acute anxiety that is both extremely serious and very frightening. In English we would call it, "life Wind" or "heart Wind."

Thangka - a Tibetan religious painting.

Tibetan Rites - a system of yogic exercises that have continuous movement.

Tipa (Bile) - one of the Three Humors of the body that represents heat. It provides the ability to strategize and discriminate, and it also helps regulate the temperature of the body, metabolic functions, and the liver. Also spelled *mKhris-pa* in many translations.

Tum-mo - the practice of altering body temperature, as practiced by some Tibetan monks.

Wind (*rLung*) - one of the Three Humors. It represents circulation in the body, such as circulation of blood and energy. It is also responsible for the circulation of thoughts in the mind.

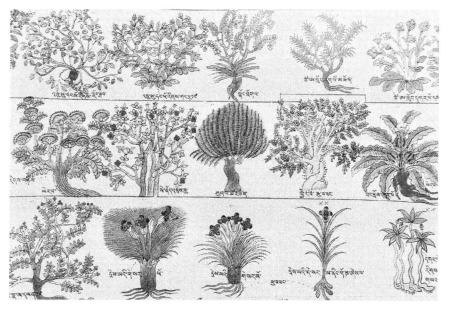

GRATITUDE

This book would not have been possible without the kind words, encouragement, patience, and wry humor of Dr. (Lady) Dadhon Jamling of the Tibetan Medical and Astro. Institute in Dharamsala, India. Dr. Jamling and I grew together. We started out as research partners measuring the efficacy of Tibetan medical treatments from the scientific and Western biomedical perspective, and in the end, became colleagues straddling both the domains of scientific research into Tibetan Medicine, and also promoting its use and understanding abroad.

My dearest thanks to Geoffrey Harrison, Phil Stewart, Brooke Thomas, Julie Abisgold, Sari Avis, Mikkel Thorup, and all my Oxford colleagues for encouraging and supporting me over the years in this field.

To my best friend, Tom Friedman, my husband. Always there for me.

This book has taken ten years to come out. It's been written in between school plays, sports games, music recitals, dinners, dishes, and running a Tibetan and Chinese herbal clinic. So my heart goes out to my family who allowed this to happen, and my dear editors at Born Perfect® Ink, who encouraged me to get this in print. Thank you all.

And to my patients . . . thank you!

ABOUT THE AUTHOR

MARY FRIEDMAN RYAN received her MSc and PhD from Oxford University in human biology and medical anthropology. From 1991-1997,

she researched the efficacy of Tibetan and Asian medical treatments in Dharamsala, India. Here, her collaborations with Dr. Jamling led to groundbreaking methodologies in efficacy research. During her postdoctoral research on the treatment of Tibetan refugees with mental health issues, Dr. Ryan was astounded by the effectiveness of Tibetan Medicine for anxiety. This inspired her to train in Tibetan and Chinese herbal medicine and acupuncture. She now practices in Greenfield, Massachusetts.

MORE ABOUT DR. (LADY) DADHON JAMLING

DR. DADHON JAMLING is a Tibetan medical doctor, and the Personal Physician to His Holiness, the Dalai Lama. She lives and works

in Deredhun, India. Throughout her extensive career in Tibetan Medicine, Dr. Dadhon's passion for the biomedical documentation of the effectiveness of Tibetan Medicine has led to several pivotal research results.

Made in the USA
Las Vegas, NV
27 May 2021